Willard Giese

THE JUNIOR SONG AND CHORUS BOOK

BY

T. P. GIDDINGS

DIRECTOR OF MUSIC, PUBLIC SCHOOLS, MINNEAPOLIS, MINNESOTA

AND

E. W. NEWTON

AUTHOR OF "MUSIC IN THE PUBLIC SCHOOLS," "PRIMARY MELODIES," ETC.

GINN AND COMPANY
BOSTON · NEW YORK · CHICAGO · LONDON
ATLANTA · DALLAS · COLUMBUS · SAN FRANCISCO

The Athenæum Press

GINN AND COMPANY · PRO-
PRIETORS · BOSTON · U.S.A.

INTRODUCTION

This book presents for young people a collection of songs and choruses which are beautiful and at the same time remarkably free from technical difficulties. It is suitable for use in the highest elementary grades or in the high school. It is an easy book for mixed schools where the adolescent voice needs special consideration. It therefore contains not only a wealth of good music by which to foster artistic growth and to develop adequate musical expression, but also music in which the boys' parts are easy and limited in compass and range.

It is designed to accompany the New Educational Music Course and may follow the Intermediate Song Reader. In order that its purpose may be more readily understood, a brief, comprehensive view of the Course is here given.

THE AIM OF THE NEW EDUCATIONAL MUSIC COURSE

The aim of this Course is to develop in the pupil an intelligent appreciation and enjoyment of good music, a musical and expressive voice, the ability to read music at sight, and the power of musical interpretation.

To inspire love of good music. To appreciate the power and beauty of music, the pupil must become familiar with well-written music of various kinds in selections that shall be interesting from his own point of view as well as admirable from that of the critical musician. By familiar association with such music and wisely directed study of it the pupil's taste is cultivated and a love of good music is fostered. With this in view the Course provides a great variety of selections culled from the best available sources.

To develop a musical voice. The proper treatment of the youthful voice is of great importance, and has received the utmost attention in these books. No elaborate scheme of voice culture is desirable or practicable in the elementary schools; but, beginning with the cultivation of the head-tone quality of the child voice through the descending scale, the few simple vital principles which induce breath control, proper tone direction, voice quality, and enunciation are presented in songs and underlie the material of the entire Course.

In each grade all selections are so placed in pitch and range as to conserve and foster the pupil's voice at that stage of his development. The aim is to establish early and thoroughly a correct use of the voice, in order that the vocal poise shall not be lost when the attention is given to the intellectual demands of sight singing.

To teach sight singing. Sight singing is the process of determining by an act of reasoning the meaning of signs in musical notation, and singing accordingly. When rightly taught, it furnishes the very essence of intellectual training and deserves to rank with any other disciplinary study.

In sight singing, deductions are made conjointly in rhythm and melody. Various intervals in melodic order, the beat, accent, tones of different duration, measure, rhythm, intermediate tones, and the minor mode — in a word, all musical effects — should be experienced before they are represented.

An abundance of attractive song material is given for reading. New problems are presented one at a time, graded in difficulty, and thus gradual mental progress is assured.

It must be borne in mind that valuable as sight singing is as a disciplinary study, it is, nevertheless, only a means to the use of music as a cultural study, and to that awakening of the æsthetic faculties which is manifested in musical interpretation.

To induce musical interpretation. Musical interpretation is the discovery and expression of the significance and beauty of musical ideas, and it therefore demands the use of material in which there are beauty and meaning to be expressed. This indispensable condition has been abundantly satisfied in the character of the music selected for this Course. Furthermore, aids to interpretation are provided not only in the marks of expression — dynamic and tempo signs, phrase and breath marks — but also in the great care with which the relation of words and music has been considered.

The character of the poem is always a key to the spirit of the music, and a thoughtful study of the verse as to accent, rhyme, phrasing, and the development of climax will reveal the rhythmical form and melodic structure of the music. The poems have been selected with quite as much care as the music, to make sure of intrinsic worth, interest, and beauty from the pupil's standpoint as well as from the literary point of view. In all cases a right and beautiful interpretation of the spirit and content of the words helps to the understanding and expression of the music.

THE MATERIAL OF THE COURSE

A distinguishing feature. A distinguishing feature of the material throughout the Course is that each number illustrates some well-known characteristic of music, racial or individual, and contains that vital quality called *musical content*, which appeals to the inexperienced learner as well as to the trained musician.

Basis of choice. Aside from the elements in notation of music, which are noted as they occur in the Course, there has been in the choice of material a constant recognition of the ideal development of the pupil. This includes the physical development resulting from deep breathing, the intellectual development involved in a systematic study of the subject, and development of character which comes from familiarity with good music.

In the Junior Song and Chorus Book the musical selections are symbolic of the varied moods and activities of youth. Opportunity for spontaneous expression will be found in songs of triumph, happiness, play, joy, peace, plaintiveness, devotion, rhythmic fancy, gayety, pathos, exhilaration, meditation, and so on.

In Part II there are occasionally introduced small notes an octave above the bass part. There are schools where the boys' voices have not changed sufficiently to enable them to sing the bass part, and these notes have been introduced so that all the songs may be available under all conditions and that boys whose voices have not yet changed may have experience in reading from the bass staff.

Grateful acknowledgment is made to Miss Helen S. Leavitt for valuable service in arranging many of the selections so that they are suitable for pupils of this period and yet lose none of their musical and harmonic content.

CONTENTS

THE JUNIOR SONG AND CHORUS BOOK

PART I

SONGS AND CHORUSES FOR UNCHANGED VOICES

March of Triumph

M. A. L. Lane

Arthur Nevin

1. Hail, ye vic - tors, home re - turn - ing,
2. Hail, ye van-quished, Worn and wea - ry!
3. Hail, ye he - roes! Life will try us,

Joy - ful that your work is done; And fill'd with pride and ex - ul - ta - tion!
Cru - el seem the shouts and cheers; And griev-ous are your wounds and bruis-es,
Both with lau - rels and with chains. But great - er is a no - ble spir - it

Fair - er fight was nev - er won. All the ills are now for - got - ten,
But re - mem - ber hap - pier years! None will dare de - spise your strug - gle,
Than the proud-est king that reigns. Calm - ly to re - trieve dis - as - ter,

All the stress and strain are o'er; Hail, tri - um - phant
All your strength ye glad - ly gave; Yours, per - haps, the
Know - ing no such word as "fail," This is val - or;

sons of for - tune! Wel - come to our ranks once more!
fin - er cour - age; Ye may be the tru - ly brave.
this is glo - ry; Hail, ye he - roes, hail, O hail!

Slumber Song

Celia Standish

Robert Schumann
Arr. from Op. 124, No. 16

1. Fierce and wild the o - cean loud is roar - ing!
2. Mid wild waves far out. up - on the o - cean,

Hush, my ba - by, nest in moth - er's arm. .
There, my ba - by, fa - ther toils for thee. .

Storm clouds dark now o'er the sky are frown - ing,
Sweet thy slum - ber, tho' the storm is rag - ing,

Hush, my ba - by, thou art safe from harm. .
Hush, my ba - by, safe you e'er may be. . .

Sunrise

Rose Alden

M. Lansen

1. Far a - way! Far a - way!
2. Far a - way! Far a - way!

1. Far a - way, a - way, O far a - way, a - way Now
2. Far a - way, a - way, O far a - way, a - way Now

Dawns the day! dawns the day!
Dawns the day! dawns the day!

dawns the day, the day, now dawns the day!
dawns the day, the day, now dawns the day!

Hail the dawn - ing! Hail the dawn - ing! All ye rap - tured birds on
Comes the morn - ing. Comes the morn - ing. Swift - ly flee the shad - ows

dim. e rit.

soar - ing wing, To the ris - ing splen - dor sing.
dim and gray. Wake, O world, and greet the day.

dim. e rit.

soar - ing wing,
dim and gray.

Love Your Neighbor

English version by M. Louise Baum

E. Jaques-Dalcroze
Arranged

Allegro moderato

The pool by the way - side is small, ver - y, ver - y

The way - side pool is ver - - - y

small, Yet it mir - rors the sun with the best of them

small, Yet shows the sun the best of

1. If the pool should grow lar - ger 'Twould not be so
all. 2. If the sea were as nar - row as you can but
3. Tho' the heart is a small thing Just love, and you'll

fair, As it smiles like an eye To the sweet sum - mer
stride, It could still rock the stars In its clear az - ure
find That there's room and to spare For the whole of man -

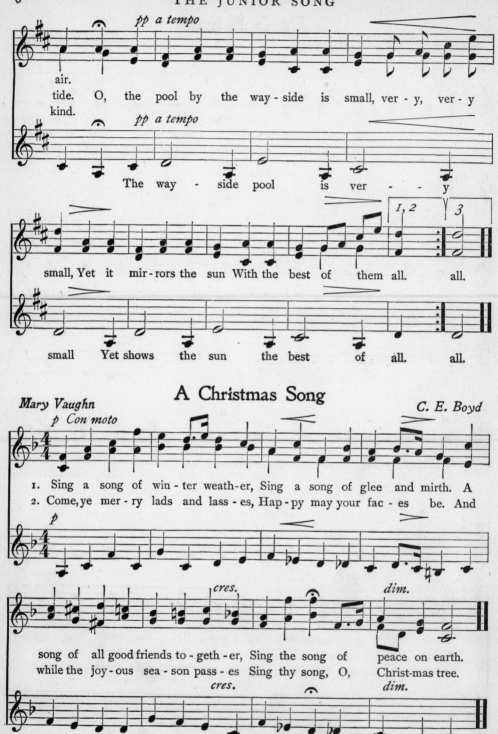

air.

tide. O, the pool by the way - side is small, ver - y, ver - y

kind.

The way - side pool is ver - y

small, Yet it mir - rors the sun With the best of them all. all.

small Yet shows the sun the best of all. all.

A Christmas Song

Mary Vaughn

C. E. Boyd

1. Sing a song of win - ter weath-er, Sing a song of glee and mirth. A
2. Come, ye mer - ry lads and lass - es, Hap - py may your fac - es be. And

song of all good friends to - geth - er, Sing the song of peace on earth.
while the joy - ous sea - son pass - es Sing thy song, O, Christ-mas tree.

The Noël Star

English version by Felix Goddard   *French Folk Tune*

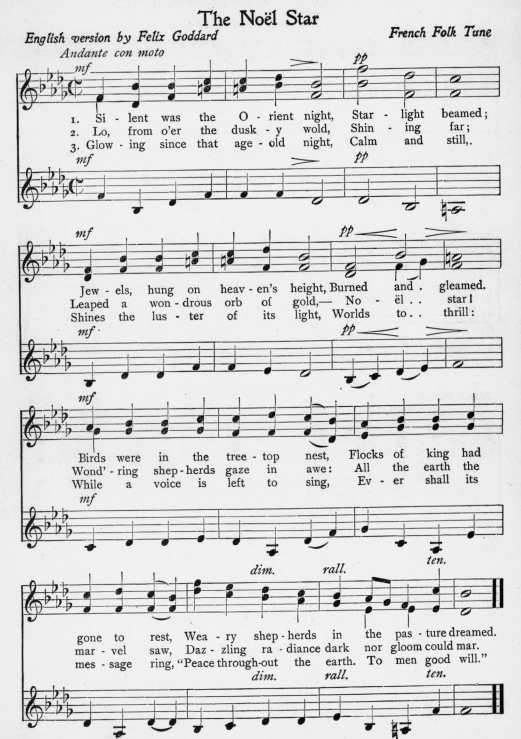

1. Si - lent was the O - rient night, Star - light beamed;
2. Lo, from o'er the dusk - y wold, Shin - ing far;
3. Glow - ing since that age - old night, Calm and still,.

Jew - els, hung on heav - en's height, Burned and . gleamed.
Leaped a won - drous orb of gold,— No - ël .. star!
Shines the lus - ter of its light, Worlds to .. thrill:

Birds were in the tree - top nest, Flocks of king had
Wond' - ring shep - herds gaze in awe: All the earth the
While a voice is left to sing, Ev - er shall its

gone to rest, Wea - ry shep - herds in the pas - ture dreamed.
mar - vel saw, Daz - zling ra - diance dark nor gloom could mar.
mes - sage ring, "Peace through-out the earth. To men good will."

Beyond the Sea

Herbert Miles

Robert Schumann
Arr. from Op. 68, No. 28

Molto cantabile

1. One vis - ion haunts me ev - er, So dear, so dear to me. 'Tis
2. 'Tis clad in trail - ing ros - es That greet the lad - en bee, And

just a lit - tle cot - tage, A home be - yond the sea.
still it calls me ev - er, That home be - yond the sea.

Devotion

Isaac Watts

John B. Dykes

Andante espressivo

1. Come, Ho - ly Spir - it, Heav'n - ly Dove, With all Thy quick'n - ing
2. Look, how we grov - el here be - low, Fond of these tri - fling
3. In vain we tune our for - mal songs, In vain we strive to

pow'rs; Kin - dle a flame of sa - cred love In these cold hearts of ours.
toys: Our souls can nei - ther fly nor go To reach e - ter - nal joys.
rise: Ho - san - nas lan - guish on our tongues, And our de - vo - tion dies.

Evening Song

Arthur Hill   English Folk Tune

Fairy Revels

Harvey Worthington Loomis

Arthur Edward Johnstone
Arr. by H. S. Leavitt

on the charm-ed ground. . .
jew-els shin-ing clear. . .

ground, charm-ed ground. . .
gems shin-ing clear. . .

ground, charm-ed ground. . .
gems shin-ing clear. . .

Faint,

leggiero

Hark! now the rip-ple of a tune is heard;

The Music of the Brook

Victor N. Pierpont   *Italian Folk Tune*

Leggiero

1. There is mu - sic in the rip - ple of the
2. There is mu - sic in the rus - tle of the

1. There is mu - sic in the
2. There is mu - sic in the

brook, now! In the cool, bright, pearl - white brook, now!
breeze, now! In the glad, spring, swift - wing breeze, now!

Where it rip - ples o'er the peb - bles, on - ly
As it plays a - mid the leaf - age of the

chat - ters in the
plays a - mid the

look, now! With a swift and stead - y flow.
trees, now! With a wild call birds all know.

On the hill - side, By the rill side, There's a
Hear it fly now, To the sky now, 'Tis a

gay, gay song as lim - pid as a flute.
weird, weird song like dry - ads where they rove.

On the moun - tain, By the foun - tain,
Ech - o on, song, Like a swan song,

Comes a tune like sound of lute.
As you die with - in the grove.

Evening Bells

Rose Alden   *Robert Allan*

1. Ring! Ring! Song of dy-ing day. Ring the sol-emn eve-ning bell. Sun-beams have fled a-way, Night brings the shad-ows gray. Ring the sol-emn eve-ning bell.

2. Ring! Ring! Song of peace and rest. Ring the sol-emn eve-ning bell. Winds whis-per from the west, Birds seek their qui-et nest. Ring the sol-emn eve-ning bell.

Woodland Pictures

Felix Goddard   *Wolfgang Amadeus Mozart*
                                                   Arranged

1. The sum-mer wood-lands dim and cool Their fra-grant per-fume

2. A shaft of sun-light darts a-cross To pierce the mist-y

yield ; Tall pines are mir - rored in the pool, Their
shades ; Its gold will dap - ple fern and moss, And

cres.

Oh hark ! Oh hark !
Ah look ! Ah look !
p

beau - ty twice re - vealed, twice re - vealed. Hark, oh hark ! A song out -
deck the flow - 'ry glades, flow - 'ry glades. Look, ah look ! The mountain

cres. *p*

A - far . . . .
O'er crag . . .
f *mp*

breaks ; The soar - ing lark the wel - kin wakes A -
stream In morn's white light a - gleam, a - gleam, O'er

f

Twice o'er . . . . .
A bright . . . .

far the ech - oes sweet, so sweet, Twice o'er his lay re - peat.
crag and rock - y steep now hurls A bright cas - cade of pearls.

Long Live Valor

English version by Mary Stanhope

Gaetano Donizetti
Arr. from the Opera "The Daughter of the Regiment"

1. My youth passed mid out-cry and up-roar of can-non; But ah! mar-tial glo-ry is e'er wrought by pain.

2. I looked long on sor-row, on fu-ror and car-nage, But ah! time has weak-ened the strong hand of hate;

By heart-break and an-guish, By
Com-pas - sion and friend-ship, Com-

heart-break and an - guish, En - dured all in vain. So
pas-sion and friend-ship Shall rule us, tho' late. So

long live the val - or That ev - er hath art, To

make the high   con-quests That sol - ace   the heart.

p   *stringendo*

Ah, . .

Ah, val - or   is vic - tor   That aye hath   the

true art   To con-quer   all   ran - cor   In pure peace of heart.

By the Fireside

Allen Harvey   *Robert Allan*

Dolce espressivo

1. Now   the   day   is   past,   Eve - ning comes   at   last;   All   our
2. Soon   the   fire - light fades   And   the   eve - ning shades Gath - er

task   and toil   is   done. Bright   the   fire - light gleam, Ev' - ry
ev - en dark - er   round. Breez - es   loud - er   sweep Through the

rud - dy beam Like a bor - rowed ray from the
for - est deep With a note of woe in the

sun. Ra - diant vi - sions, bright With fan - cy's light Come
sound. Twink - ling em - bers lie, All loath to die, As

troop - ing at the fire - light's call; Sil - ver - sweet and clear The fair - y
one by one the mo - ments creep. From the ash - es gray We soft - ly

songs we hear As the twi - light shad - ows fall.
steal a - way To a land of dreams and sleep.

Spring Morning

Charles Harvey

Stanley R. Avery

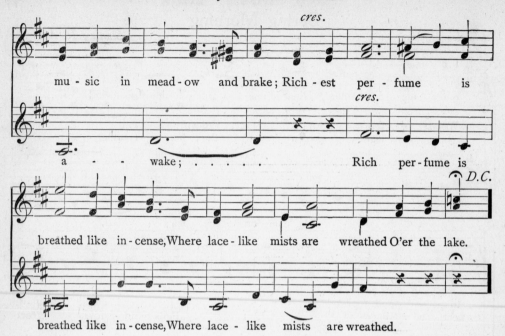

cres.

music in mead-ow and brake; Rich-est per-fume is

cres.

a - - wake; . . . . . Rich per-fume is

D.C.

breathed like in-cense, Where lace-like mists are wreathed O'er the lake.

breathed like in-cense, Where lace-like mists are wreathed.

The Cossack's Lullaby

Translated

N. Bachmetieff

pp Tranquillo

1. Sleep, ah, sleep, my dar - ling ba - by, Su, su,
2. O - ver fields and stones is rush - ing Wild the
3. And a war - rior like thy fa - ther Thou shalt

pp

lul - la - by; (lul - la - by;) . See, the moon is
storm at night; (lul - la - by;) . While the war - rior
one day be; (lul - la - by;) . Ah! could I in

watch - ing o'er thee Peace-ful - ly on high. (lul - la - by.)
fierce is near - ing, With his weap-ons bright. (lul - la - by.)
time of dan - ger Ev - er be with thee. (lul - la - by.)

Thou shalt hear a won - drous sto - ry; Close thy
Ah! thy fa - ther fall'n in bat - tle Now is
Man - y a tear shall I be weep - ing When thy

wake - ful eye; (lul - la - by. .) And a song as
gone for aye; (lul - la - by. .) Sleep, ah, sleep, my
feet march by; (lul - la - by. .) Sleep, my ba - by,

well I'll sing thee, Su, su, lul - la - by. (lul - la - by.)
dar - ling ba - by, Su, su, lul - la - by. (lul - la - by.)
sleep in peace, now, Su, su, lul - la - by. (lul - la - by.)

Vacation

Joan Luther

L. S. Wilson

1. Come in the morn-ing, when bright is the sky; Or come . in the gloam-ing, when dark-ness is nigh; . There is sol - ace and joy in each hour of the

2. Sweet is the fra-grance of bal - sam and pine, And sweet . the wild rose and the blos - som - ing vine; . There is peace on the land and a hush on the

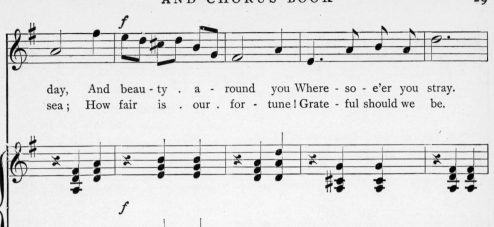

day, And beau - ty . a - round you Where - so - e'er you stray.
sea; How fair is . our . for - tune! Grate - ful should we be.

Far from the tu - mult of life you may rest, Cooled by the
Think of the noise and the heat of the town; Think of the

o - cean or rocked on its breast;   Filled with the glo - ry of
glare of the sun beat - ing down;   Would that our com - fort all

for - est and sea,   How good is mere liv - ing — how
toil - ers might share,   Re - joic - ing with us in this

hap - py and free! O then come in the morn - ing, when
life - giv - ing air! O how sweet is the fra - grance of

bright is the sky; Or come . in the gloam-ing, when dark-ness is
bal - sam and pine! How sweet . the wild rose and the blos - som - ing

nigh; There is sol - ace and joy in each hour of the
vine! There is peace on the land and a hush o'er the

day, And beau - ty a - round you Wher - e'er your feet may stray.
sea. Oh, fair is our for - tune! How grate - ful we should be!

The Tides

Herbert Miles

Stanley R. Avery

1. End - less tides, they rise and fall, Soft to the fish - er
2. End - less tides, they rise and fall; Weep - ing, the wom - en

folk they call, "Launch your boat on the wave to - day.
mourn and call, "Give them back from your wa - ters deep.

Launch your boat on the wa - ter gray." Tides, so cold and
Give them back from their qui - et sleep." Tides, so cold and

cru - el, Cease, oh cease your call.
cru - el, Cease, oh cease your call.

Rest

Franz Abt
Opus 186

1. The sun-set-light is dy - ing, The woods are si - lent
2. The arch of heav'n grows clear - er, The si - lent night draws

1. The sun-set-light is dy - ing, The woods are si - lent
2. The arch of heav'n grows clear - er, The si - lent night draws

1. The sun - set-light is dy - ing, The woods are si - lent
2. The arch of heav'n grows clear - er, The si - lent night draws

ly - ing, But that a - mong the trees.... doth
near - er, And there on high, a - far, ... doth

ly - ing, a - mong the trees doth
near - er, on high, a - far, doth

ly - ing, But that a - mong the trees.... doth
near - er, And there on high, a - far, ... doth

sigh the eve-ning breeze. . A - far the sounds are fad - ing, The
gleam the eve-ning star. . . The night-in-gales are sing - ing, My

sigh the eve-ning breeze. . A - far the sounds are fad - ing, The
gleam the eve-ning star. . . The night-in-gales are sing - ing, My

sigh the eve-ning breeze. . A - far the sounds are fad - ing, The
gleam the eve-ning star. . . The night-in-gales are sing - ing, My

bus - y day per - vad - ing, And all at rest would
soul its way is wing - ing, That ne'er on earth knew

bus - y day per - vad - ing, And all at rest would
soul its way is wing - ing, That ne'er on earth knew

bus - y day per - vad - ing, And all at rest would
soul its way is wing - ing, That ne'er on earth knew

be. . . . .   O heart, where's rest   for thee? O heart, . . .
rest, ...   to realms that Love hath blest, to realms . . .

be. . . .   O heart, where's rest   for thee?   where's
rest, ...   to realms that Love hath blest,   that

be.   O heart, where's rest . . . .   for thee?   where's
rest,   to realms that Love . . . .   hath blest,   that

. . where's rest for thee?
. . that Love hath blest.

rest   for . . thee?
Love   hath . blest.

rest   for . . thee?
Love   hath . blest.

The Heart Flower

Robert Graham

C. E. Boyd

cres.

see but tears That glis - ten in its eye." . The
tears I viewed Were gems might crown a king." . The

see but tears That glis - ten in its eye." .
tears I viewed Were gems might crown a king." .

f

min - strel sang, "'Tis like a tune That ech - oes to the
min - strel said, "The tune I heard A - woke my heart to

He sang, "'Tis like a tune That ech - oes to the
He said, "The tune I heard A - woke my heart to

sky." . "'Tis like a dream
sing." . No flow'r so fair

p

sky." . The po - et spoke, "'Tis like a dream That
sing." . The po - et spoke, "No flow'r so fair E'er

mp

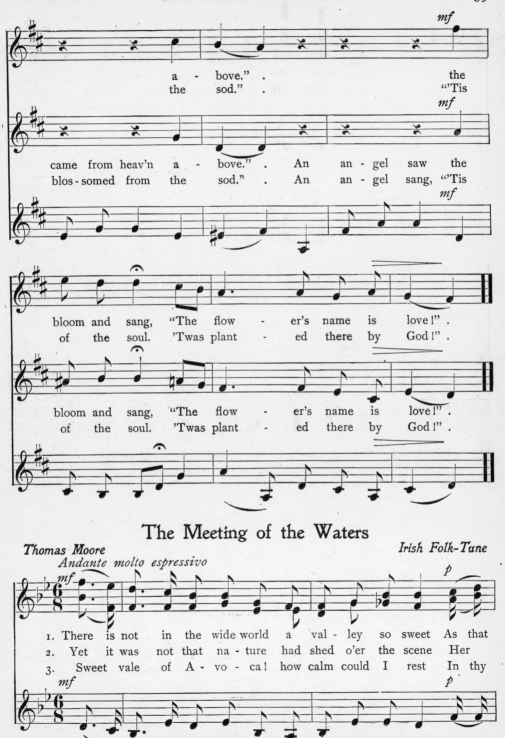

a - bove." .
the sod." .
the
"'Tis

came from heav'n a - bove." . An an - gel saw the
blos - somed from the sod." . An an - gel sang, "'Tis

bloom and sang, "The flow - er's name is love!" .
of the soul. 'Twas plant - ed there by God!" .

bloom and sang, "The flow - er's name is love!" .
of the soul. 'Twas plant - ed there by God!" .

The Meeting of the Waters

Thomas Moore

Irish Folk-Tune

Andante molto espressivo

1. There is not   in the wide world   a   val - ley   so sweet   As that
2. Yet   it was   not that   na - ture   had shed o'er the scene   Her
3. Sweet   vale   of A - vo - ca!   how calm could I   rest   In thy

vale in whose bo - som the bright wa - ters meet. Oh! the
pur - est of crys - tal and bright - est of green; 'Twas
bo - som of shade with the friends I love best; Where the

last rays of feel - ing and life must de - part Ere the
not her soft mag - ic of stream - let or hill, Oh, . .
storms that we feel in this cold world would cease, And our

bloom of that val - ley shall fade from my heart, Ere the
no! it was some - thing more ex - qui - site still, Oh, . .
hearts like thy wa - ters, be min - gled in peace, And our

bloom of that val - ley shall fade from my heart.
no! it was some - thing more ex - qui - site still.
hearts like thy wa - ters, be min - gled in peace.

Folk Dance

Allan Shaw

Gabriel Marie

Arr. from " La Cinquantaine " by H. S. Leavitt

1. O come, ye lads and lass - es gay, Take your play - time while ye may, While the sunshine gilds the day, Be - fore all is gray. The air is fresh like draughts of dew, Na - ture builds her

2. O clear - er, clear - er rings the lay, No one here is old to - day, All are sing-ing, all are gay, And life seems but play. In wait - ing ranks the danc - ers stand, Swing - ing, sway - ing,

world a - new,   Come, all   ye whose hearts are   sore, and
hand in hand,   Hark! a   lilt - ing meas - ure sounds and

sigh   no more.   Old and young a - like must join us,
joy   a - bounds.   See them now, the rib - bons fling - ing,

Dance and sing and play,   No one should be
Weave a mys-tic chain,   Close a-round the

Dance and sing and play, and sing and play.
Weave a mys-tic chain, a mys-tic chain.

sad or tear-ful, None should grieve to-day.
may-pole cling-ing, Then un-twine a-gain!

And none should grieve to-day, should grieve to-
And then un-twine a-gain, un-twine a-

mf

Strains of wild bar - bar - ic mu - sic Lure the chil - dren's
Ma - trons flush with ea - ger pleas - ure, Men look on with

day. Bar - bar - ic mu - sic lure the
gain. The ma - trons flush with joy and

feet to stay, To re - gions en - chant - ed they
ten - der smiles While mem - 'ry their fan - cy be

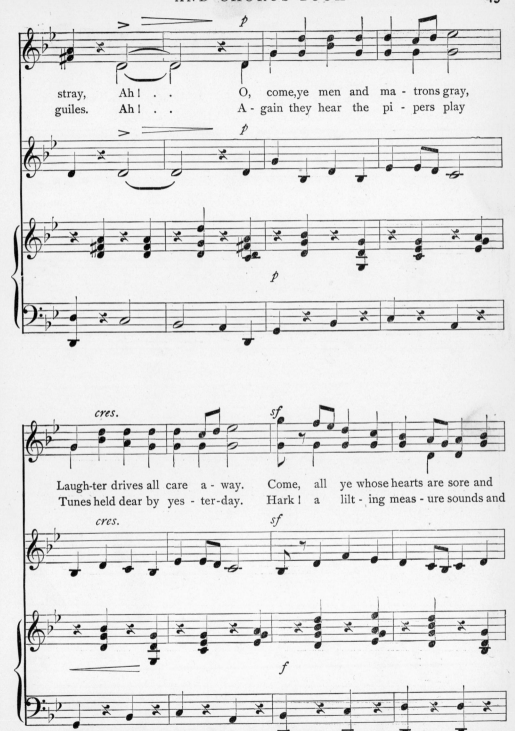

stray, Ah! . . O, come, ye men and ma - trons gray,
guiles. Ah! . . A - gain they hear the pi - pers play

Laugh-ter drives all care a - way. Come, all ye whose hearts are sore and
Tunes held dear by yes - ter-day. Hark! a lilt - ing meas - ure sounds and

sigh   no   more.   Ring - ing voic - es greet the hap - py
joy   a - bounds.   Chil - dren's voic - es break the mag - ic

crowd ;   Then come, ye lads and lass - es gay, Let no   one here be
spell—   Now clear - er, clear - er rings the lay, And all are sing - ing

sad to-day, Let no one here be sad to-day, For oh! 'tis
all are gay, And all are sing-ing, all are gay, For oh! 'tis

May! May! But joys will end, how-ev-er bright, And

dark - 'ning skies an - nounce the night.

dark   the night.   Hark to the call, ye lads and

lass - es gay, 'tis   Ah,   come,   For

lass - es gay, E'er yet we take our home - ward way, For

soon will sound the ves - per bell, And we must say Fare-well.

Faint-Heart

Joan Luther

Mabel C. Osborne

Pensieroso

1. On - ward the . riv - er flows, New flow'rs will
2. Ev - er the . wa - ter flows; Ev - er it

deck its way; But here droops a . .
keeps its way; For no drop that .

ten - der rose that fain would beg   Time to
sea - ward flows would dare to loi - ter or

stay— Ah, no! Brave hearts that face the day,
stray— Ah, no! Look up, my lit - tle flow'r!

Fear - ing   no hurt or harm,   How can ye
All's fair and green a - round. You too shall

best al - lay her doubt and a - larm?
have your hour; by love shall be crowned.

A Farewell

Charles Kingsley

Andante

George H. Gartlan

My fair - est child, I have no song to give you; .

. . No lark could pipe to skies so dull and gray;

Yet, ere we part, one les - son I can leave you, . one

les - son . . for ev - 'ry day. . . . . Be good, sweet

ev - 'ry day.

maid, and let who will be clev - er. . . Do no - ble

things, not dream them all day long. . . And so make

life, death, and that vast for - ev - er . . One grand, one

song. . . . .

grand sweet song, one grand sweet song, one grand sweet song.

PART II

SONGS AND CHORUSES FOR SOPRANO, ALTO AND BASS

Sing!

Rose Alden
mf con moto
dim.
p cres.
Phyllis Brunt

1. Sing! Let us sing! Oh, the world is made for song and laugh-ter.
2. Sing! Let us sing! What if shade and trou-ble fol-low aft-er.

mf
dim.

mf

Sing! Let us sing! Bright-ly shines the gold-en day.
Sing! Let us sing! We will drive all care a-way.

mf

The Star

Mary Webster
mf Allegretto
M. Bellingham

1. Once up-on a bright spring morn-ing, Clear the birds sang, near and far,
2. When the sum-mer days were dawn-ing, Gold-en sun-shine, sil-ver rain.

mf

dim.
p
star.
lain.

Down a-mong the sway-ing grass-es Fell a shin-ing, shin-ing star.
Smiled a gold-en-heart-ed dai-sy Where the star had lain, had lain.

dim.
p

The Match Game

Allan Shaw   *S. Hoffer*

Allegro con spirito

1. Oh, the
2. We will

day is here, and the sky is clear, And we're off with ban-ners

fight this fight and we'll do it right, But if e - vil things be-

fly - ing! Our game is strong, and we shan't go wrong For the

tide us, We look to you to be staunch and true When the

lack of ear-nest try-ing. We're fair-ly matched, and we
fic-kle crowd de-ride us. We won't com-plain, we will

have no fears; We'll show you pluck and dar-ing; And you'll
play the game, What-e'er the wind and weath-er; And the

make us feel by your heart-y cheers That ev-'ry gain you're shar-ing.
school need fear no de-feat or shame Be-cause we'll work to-geth-er.

Watchman's Song

Herbert Miles

Edvard Grieg
Arr. from Op. 12, No. 3

Molto andante e semplice

1. The night is dark and drear - y, Watch-man, on thy guard! Tho'
2. The sol-diers all are sleep - ing, Watch-man, on thy guard! Their

hard thy lot and wea - ry, Watch-man, on thy guard! Be-
safe - ty thou art keep - ing, Watch-man, on thy guard! The

hold the stars keep guard on high, And share thy watch from the
foe now o'er the hill ap - pears. See! his proud ban - ner on

See the stars keep
Foe now o'er the

kind - ly sky. The night is dark and drear - y, Watch-man, on thy guard!
high he rears. The sol-diers all are sleep - ing, Watch-man, on thy guard!

The Rose Bush

Mary Vaughn

Eugene Adams

1. Shad - ed and cool is the flow - er - ing gar - den; Dust - y and hot is the neigh - bor - ing street, And o - ver the wall climb the ram - bling ros - es, Giv - ing the pass - ers a fra - grance sweet.

2. Pleas - ant the paths of the green shad - ed gar - den, Birds there are sing - ing at morn - ing and noon. But o - ver the wall climb the ram - bling ros - es, Bring - ing the pass - ers a breath of June.

Dear Harp of My Country

Thomas Moore

Welsh Folk Tune

1. Dear Harp of my . Coun-try, in dark-ness. I . found thee; The cold chain of . si-lence had hung o'er thee long, When proud-ly, my . own Is-land Harp, I . un-twine. bound thee, And gave all thy chords to light, free-dom and song!

2. Dear Harp of my . Coun-try, fare-well to . thy num-bers, This sweet wreath of . song is the last we shall twine. Go, sleep with the . sun-shine of fame on . thy . slum-bers, Till touched by some hand less un-worth-y than mine.

The . warm lay . of . love and the light note of .
If the pulse of . the pa - tri - ot, sol - dier or .

glad - ness Have wak - ened thy fond - est, thy live - li - est
lov - er Have throbb'd at . our lay, 'tis thy glo - ry a -

thrill; But so oft hast thou ech - oed the deep sigh of
lone; It was but as the wind pass - ing heed - less - ly

sad - ness, That e'en in thy mirth it will steal from thee still.
o - ver, And all the wild sweet - ness I waked was thy own.

Night

Rose Alden

Robert Schumann
Arr. from Op. 12, No. 5

1. Sleep! sleep! Si-lent town! Sleep! sleep! God looks down! A-bove thy
2. Sleep! sleep! Dreaming town! Sleep! sleep! Clouds may frown. Tho' storms may

head shine on high, Faith-ful stars in His own sky.
come, soon they're gone, Aft-er dark-ness God gives dawn.

Spring Song

Allan Shaw

Elizabeth Faye

1. March has sent his breez-es fly-ing Through the frost-y air,
2. A-pril, we are tired of win-ter; Bring thy gay-est flow'rs;
3. Tinged with morn-ing's glow-ing splen-dor, Fleec-y clouds are bright;

Driv-en off the snow in tri-umph, Made earth bright and fair.
Thou shalt have a roy-al wel-come, Month of sun and show'rs!
Spring, with view-less fin-gers ten-der, Lifts her blos-soms white.

March of the Seasons

Celia Standish

C. E. Boyd

1. March - ing, march - ing, on - ward march - ing,
2. March - ing, march - ing, on - ward march - ing,

On the end - less sea - sons go. Time of bud and
Pass - ing on with stead - y tread. Told by rose and

bee and blos - som, Time of fruit and drift - ing snow.
fall - ing snow-flake, Count - less a - ges all have sped.

Castles in the Air

Rudolph Krüger

1. Blow, . O blow, . ye win - ter wind! A blaz - ing hearth we sit be - side; We're build - ing cas - tles in the air, With loft - y towers be - yond com - pare, And ban - ners float - ing wide. .

2. Dreams, ah, dreams, yes, i - dle dreams! Yet full con - tent the dream - ers know. Though time may fill their lives with care, They still have seen a vis - ion fair With - in the fire - light's glow. .

How Can I Leave Thee

Helmine von Chezy
Translated

Friedrich Kücken

1. How can I leave thee! How can I from thee part!
2. Blue is a flow'r - et Called the "For - get - me - not,"
3. Would I a bird were! Soon at thy side to be;

Thou on - ly hast my heart, Sis - ter, be - lieve.
Wear it up - on thy heart, And think of me!
Fal - con nor hawk would fear Speed - ing to thee.

Thou hast this soul of mine So close - ly bound to thine,
Flow'r - et and hope may die, Yet love with us shall stay,
When by the fow - ler slain, I at thy feet should lie,

No oth - er can I love, Save thee a - lone!
That can - not pass a - way, Sis - ter, be - lieve.
Thou sad - ly shouldst com - plain, Joy - ful I'd die.

Awake, My Soul

Philip Doddridge

Arr. from George Frederick Handel

1. A - wake, my soul, stretch ev - 'ry nerve, And press with vig - or on; . A heav'n - ly race de - mands thy . zeal, And an im - mor - tal crown, And an im - mor - tal crown.
2. A cloud of wit - ness - es a - round Hold thee in full sur - vey: . For - get the steps al - read - y . trod, And on - ward urge thy way, . And on - ward urge thy way.
3. That prize, with peer - less glo - ries bright, Which shall new lus - ter boast, When vic - tor's wreaths and mon - arch's gems Shall blend in com - mon dust, . Shall blend in . com - mon dust.

The Lonely Linnet

English version by Louise Stickney

Italian Folk Tune

Allegretto

mp

ff

1. The lin-net to his love was sing - ing
2. The owl now said in stern and sol - emn
3. The lin-net came at last, though scarce - ly

light - ly, Was sing - ing to her bright - ly, ev - 'ry
warn - ing, "If you would not go mourn - ing, mend your
hop - ing. He thought to find her mop - ing or dis -

night. . . She flout - ed him and mocked him im - po -
ways ! . . Your lov - er was too faith - ful for such
traught. . And lo, she met him, kind and gay and

lite - ly, Her cru - el - ty was shame - ful, far - from
scorn - ing; He ought to leave you lone - ly all your
smil - ing, With look and tone be - guil - ing, claim - ing

right ;   At   last   he   flew   a - way   and   left   her

days !   Of   course he's   gone ; he   could   not   stay   for -

naught ;   "O   nev - er   go   a - way   a - gain,   dear

lone - ly,   She   heard   the   drear - y   owl's   "Too - whit !   too

ev - er,   Too   clev - er   he,   to   beg   and   pray   and

Lin - net !   Your   song   is   sweet - er   far   than   all   the

whoo!" "O Lin - net dear, re - turn! I love you
sue." "You cru - el bird! I nev - er liked you,—
rest. My fa - vor shall be yours; you'll sure - ly

on - ly. I'm fright-ened here a - lone. Oh, where are you?"
nev - er! The glass - es you are wear - ing must be blue."
win it, If on - ly you will stay be - side my nest!"

Oh, Beware!

English version by Felix Goddard

Folk Tune

1. Oh, be-ware! Oh, be-ware! Tho' the rose .. be fair,
2. Oh, be-ware! Oh, be-ware! Tho' the gold - en bee
3. Oh, be-ware! Oh, be-ware! Red the i - - vy glows;

Tho' its per-fume sweet is . borne On the dew - y air of morn,
Thro' the gar - den tak - eth wing, Tho' he soft - ly hum and sing,
Yet your per - il will be - gin, When that flam - ing

Have a care! Have a care! Lurks a cru - el thorn.
Have a care! Have a care! Lurks a cru - el sting.

spray you win. Have a care! Have a care! Poi - son lurks there-in.

Voices of Autumn

Celia Standish

Mabel C. Osborne

1. I can hear the Bob White call - ing, clear call - ing,
2. I can hear the brook's low sing - ing, low sing - ing,

clear call - ing, I can hear the chest - nuts fall -
low sing - ing, I can see the swal - lows wing -

ing; Thro' the leaves they are rat - tling down. And the ha - zy sun is
ing O'er the roofs of the dream-ing town. To the far - off South - land

dream - ing, is dream - ing, is dream - ing, Thro' the
fly - ing, swift fly - ing, swift fly - ing. For the

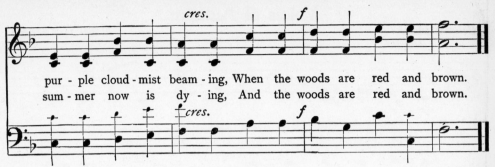

pur - ple cloud - mist beam - ing, When the woods are red and brown.
sum - mer now is dy - ing, And the woods are red and brown.

A Petition

John G. Whittier   Frederick C. Maker

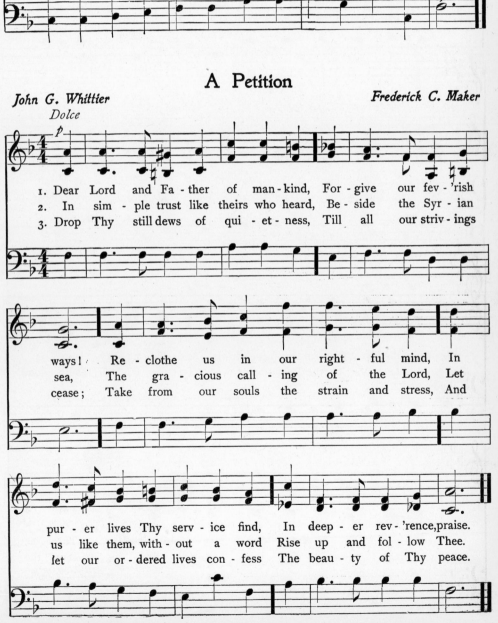

1. Dear Lord and Fa - ther of man - kind, For - give our fev - 'rish
2. In sim - ple trust like theirs who heard, Be - side the Syr - ian
3. Drop Thy still dews of qui - et - ness, Till all our striv - ings

ways! Re - clothe us in our right - ful mind, In
sea, The gra - cious call - ing of the Lord, Let
cease; Take from our souls the strain and stress, And

pur - er lives Thy serv - ice find, In deep - er rev - 'rence, praise.
us like them, with - out a word Rise up and fol - low Thee.
let our or - dered lives con - fess The beau - ty of Thy peace.

The Sea Gull

Herbert Miles

Edouard Batiste
Arranged

1. Rise o'er the bil - lows, wand - 'ring sea - gull, Beat the keen
2. Why art thou cry - ing? What will harm thee? Thou hast no

air with those pin - ions of white! . . O,
fear when the hur - ri - canes roar. . . Then

spir - it of free - dom, strong and wild, Far a -
take up thy jour - ney, fear - ing naught! Ev - er

way, far a - way, A - bove the o - cean take thy flight!
free, brave and free, The sea is thine from shore to shore.

The Willow and the Oak

A. J. Foxwell

Norwegian Folk Tune

Con espressione

1. Be - side the riv - er flow - ing, A state - ly oak there
2. With pride his head he lift - ed, When lo! the breez - es

grow - ing, Spoke to a wil - low tree. "The gen - tle breeze can
shift - ed; A storm be - gan to blow. The wil - low bent be -

bend thee, One fierc - er blast would end thee. A
fore it; At first the oak rose o'er it; The

poco rit.

gale could not harm me, A gale could not harm me."
winds then laid him low, The winds then laid him low.

poco rit.

The Tinker's Song

Charles Dibdin

1. A tink - er I am, my name's Nat - ty Dan, From
2. Those a - mong the great who tink - er the State, And
3. The man of war, the man of the bar, Phy -

morn till night I trudge it; So low is my fate, my
bad - ger the mi - nor - i - ty,— Pray what is the end of their
si - cians, priests and think - ers, That rove up and down great

ff parlando

pers - 'nal es - tate Lies all with - in this bud - get.
work, my friend, But to win a good ma - jor - i - ty.
Lon - don town,—What are they all but tink - ers?

pp colla voce

Work for the tink - ers, ho! good wives, For they are lads of

met - tle;   'Twere well if   you could mend your lives   As

I   can mend a   ket - tle,   'Twere well   if   you   could

mend your lives   As   I   can mend a   ket - tle.

mend your lives As

I can mend a ket-tle.

The Harp That Once Thro' Tara's Halls

Thomas Moore

Irish Folk Tune

Molto moderato

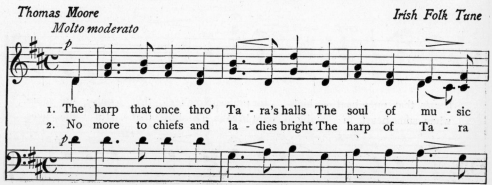

1. The harp that once thro' Ta - ra's halls The soul of mu - sic
2. No more to chiefs and la - dies bright The harp of Ta - ra

shed, . . Now hangs as mute on Ta - ra's walls As
swells; . . The chord a - lone, that breaks at night, Its

if that soul were fled! . . . . So sleeps the pride of
tale of ru - in tells; . . . . Thus Free - dom now so

for - mer days, So glo - ry's thrill is o'er, . . And
sel - dom wakes, The on - ly throb she gives, . . Is

hearts that once beat high for praise, Now feel that pulse no more.
when some heart in - dig - nant breaks, To show that still she lives.

All Through the Night

Translated

Welsh Folk-Song

1. Sleep, my child, and peace at-tend thee, All through the night,
2. While the morn her watch is keep-ing All through the night,

Guar-dian an-gels God will send thee, All through the night.
While the wea-ry world is sleep-ing, All through the night.

Soft the drow-sy hours are creep-ing, Hill and vale in slum-ber steep-ing,
O'er thy spir-it gen-tly steal-ing, Vi-sion of de-light re-veal-ing,

I my lov-ing vig-il keep-ing, All thro' the night.
Breathes a pure and ho-ly feel-ing, All thro' the night.

Autumn Winds

Laura Gary

Mary Eloise Crane

The last brown leaf on the ma-ple tree, Sad and wrin-kled and lone, ... Called low to the pass-ing wind so

dim.

"Whirl me to my win - ter home, my

free . . . .

dim. e rit.

home. Whirl . me to my win - ter home. .

Sing

Alfred Phillips

Gustav Hölzel

Moderato

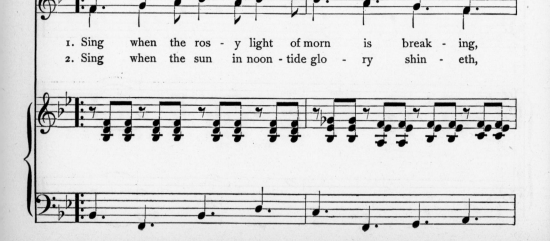

1. Sing   when   the   ros - y   light   of morn   is   break - ing,
2. Sing   when   the   sun   in noon - tide glo - ry   shin - eth,

When ev - 'ry bird and flow'r to life is wak - ing,
Or in the soft - er glow when day de - clin - eth,

Sing! and thy heart - felt lay . . . . . . Shall
Sing! for the whole day long . . . . . . May be

glad   the . . op' - ning   day.
bright   with   the voice   of   day.

song,   May   be   bright . . . .

with their voice .. of song. . . . .

Care press - eth light - er, Hope beam - eth bright - er,

Joy like a flow' - ret bloom - eth fair - - er;

Charm'd by the glad - ness, Songs bring for sad - ness,

Earth sweet - er grows and heav'n is clear - - er!

Sing then, per-chance some sor - row'd heart may hear thee,

Song oft hath sol - ace for the worn and wea - ry;

Sing on thro' life's long day, Ah! . . sing

grief   and   care   a - way,   Sing grief and

care, ...   Sing grief and care a - way ! . . . .

On the Chapel Steps

J. N. Eno

Arthur Thomas and Caspar G. Dickson

G. C. Gow

1. Here at the pleas - ant twi - light hour, When dai - ly tasks are o'er, . . We gath - er on the chap - el steps To sing our songs once more. . The braid - ed branch - es of the elms In si - lence bend to hear, . And

2. When far a - way in fu - ture days, Life's sur - feit on us falls; . When vig - ils cease and tur - moil stays, These i - vy - man - tled walls . From ev - 'ry soft - ly wav - ing leaf Will send some sooth - ing strain . To

3. And so, though far from col - lege halls We sing our songs once more; . To cheer our hearts with mem - 'ries fond Of days that are of yore, . Those days and years with pleas - ure bright, Passed by on pin - ions fleet, . But

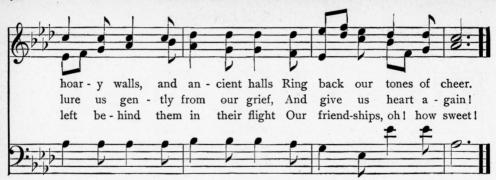

hoar - y walls, and an - cient halls Ring back our tones of cheer.
lure us gen - tly from our grief, And give us heart a - gain!
left be - hind them in their flight Our friend-ships, oh! how sweet!

Come, Sound His Praise

Isaac Watts

Isaac Smith

1. Come, sound His praise a - broad, And hymns of
2. He formed the deeps, un - known; He gave the

glo - ry .. sing: Je - ho - vah is the
seas . their . bound; The wa - t'ry worlds are

sov - 'reign . God, The u - ni - ver - sal King.
all . His .. own, And all ... the sol - id ground.

The Loreley

Heinrich Heine
Translated

Friedrich Silcher

1. I know not what it mean - eth, That
2. A fair . and love - ly maid - en Doth
3. A boat - man whose skiff so ti - ny, The

I so sad should be, .. A leg - end old and
sit up - on the height; She combs her gold - en
wa - ter deep doth lave, . En - tranced by song and

plain - tive Is ev - er haunt - ing me. The
tress - es; Her jew - els daz - zle the sight. Her
sing - er, Heeds not the rock nor the wave. I

air ... is cool, the day wan - eth, And
gold - en comb . too, glis - tens And
fear ... the craft and the boat - man En -

calm - ly flows the Rhine; . . . . The top of the moun - tain
as she combs her hair, . . . She sings a song so
gulfed by bil - lows high, . . . Be - cause of the Lore - ley's

gleam - eth, For still the sun doth shine. .
won - drous, Its rich tones fill the air. . .
sing - ing Be - neath the wave may lie. . .

Invitation

Isaac Watts
Con anima

Aaron Williams

1. Come we that love the Lord And let our joys be known;
2. Let those re - fuse to sing That nev - er knew our God;
3. Then let our songs a - bound And ev - 'ry tear be dry;

Join in a song with sweet ac - cord, And thus sur-round the throne.
But chil - dren of the heav'n-ly King May speak their joys a - broad.
We're march-ing through Em - man-uel's ground To fair - er worlds on high.

PART III

SONGS AND CHORUSES WITH BASS AD LIBITUM

A Lullaby

Joan Luther

Andante

Moritz Moszkowski
Arr. from Opus 38, No. 2

Fair Napoli

English version by Louise Stickney

Neapolitan Folk Tune

Cantabile espressivo

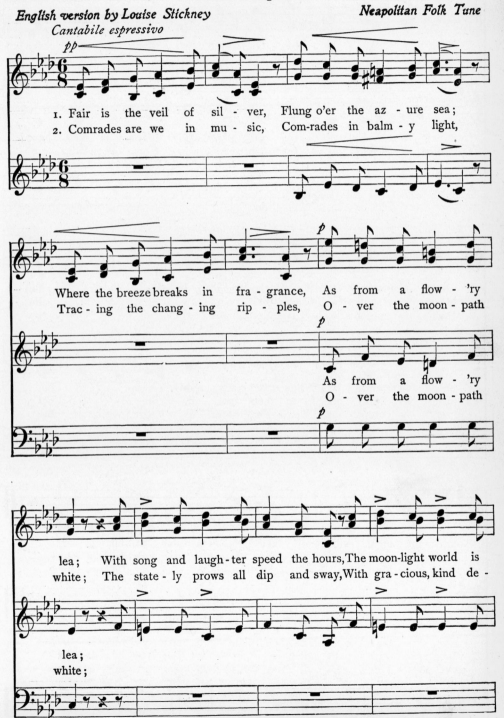

1. Fair is the veil of sil - ver, Flung o'er the az - ure sea;
2. Comrades are we in mu - sic, Com-rades in balm - y light,

Where the breeze breaks in fra - grance, As from a flow - 'ry
Trac - ing the chang - ing rip - ples, O - ver the moon - path

As from a flow - 'ry
O - ver the moon - path

lea; With song and laugh - ter speed the hours, The moon-light world is
white; The state - ly prows all dip and sway, With gra - cious, kind de -

lea;
white;

America the Beautiful [1]

Katharine Lee Bates

Arthur S. Kendall

Con spirito

1. O beau-ti-ful for spa-cious skies, For am-ber waves of
2. O beau-ti-ful for pil-grim feet, Whose stern, im-pass-ioned
3. O beau-ti-ful for he-roes proud In lib-er-at-ing
4. O beau-ti-ful for pa-triot dream That sees be-yond the

1. O beau-ti-ful for spa-cious skies, For am-ber
2. O beau-ti-ful for pil-grim feet, Whose stern, im-
3. O beau-ti-ful for he-roes proud In lib-er-
4. O beau-ti-ful for pa-triot dream That sees be-

grain, For pur-ple moun-tain ma-jes-ties A-bove the fruit-ed
stress A tho-rough-fare for free-dom beat A-cross the wil-der-
strife, Who more than self their coun-try loved, And mer-cy more than
years Thine al-a-bas-ter cit-ies gleam Im-mac-u-late of

waves of grain, For pur-ple moun-tain ma-jes-ties A-bove the
pass-ioned stress A tho-rough-fare for free-dom beat A-cross the
at-ing strife, Who more than self their coun-try loved, And mer-cy
yond the years Thine al-a-bas-ter cit-ies gleam Im-mac-u-

[1] Without the bass this is complete in three parts,—with the bass it is complete in four parts, or with the two upper voices and the bass it is complete in three parts.

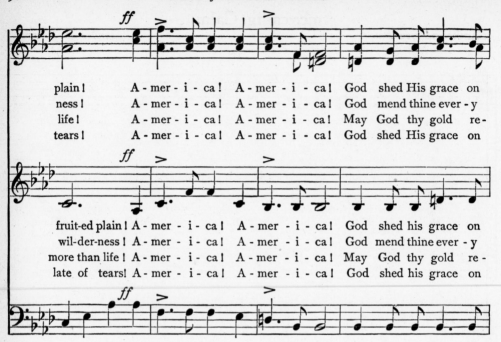

plain !   A - mer - i - ca ! A - mer - i - ca ! God   shed His grace on
ness !   A - mer - i - ca ! A - mer - i - ca ! God   mend thine ever - y
life !   A - mer - i - ca ! A - mer - i - ca ! May God thy gold   re-
tears !   A - mer - i - ca ! A - mer - i - ca ! God   shed His grace on

fruit-ed plain ! A - mer - i - ca ! A - mer - i - ca ! God   shed his grace on
wil-der-ness !   A - mer - i - ca ! A - mer - i - ca ! God   mend thine ever - y
more than life ! A - mer - i - ca ! A - mer - i - ca ! May God thy gold   re -
late of tears!   A - mer - i - ca ! A - mer - i - ca ! God   shed his grace on

thee,   And crown thy good with broth - er - hood From sea to shin - ing sea.
flaw,   Con- firm thy soul in self - con - trol, Thy lib - er - ty   in law !
fine,   Till all suc- cess be no - ble - ness, And ever - y gain di - vine !
thee,   And crown thy good with broth - er - hood From sea to shin - ing sea.

thee,   And crown thy good with broth - er - hood From sea to shin - ing sea.
flaw,   Con- firm thy soul in self - con - trol, Thy lib - er - ty   in law !
fine,   Till all   suc- cess be no - ble - ness, And ever - y gain di - vine !
thee,   And crown thy good with broth - er - hood From sea to shin - ing sea.

Evening Calm

Charles Harvey

Stanley R. Avery

1. Peace thro' the vale! Lake - side and dale Lie tranced in slum - ber 'neath the star; Waves nor winds the si - lence mar; Dream-ing gar-dens, near and far, Per - fume ex - hale.
2. Hour sweet - ly blest! Birds in the nest Have sung their last faint eve - ning hymn; Day lies couched in sha-dows dim, 'Neath the far ho - ri-zon's rim; Earth is at rest.

O What Joy

Translated and adapted by M. A. L. Lane

Charles Gounod
Arr. from the Grand Opera "Faust"

1. O what joy, O what joy, does the night hold in keep - ing? What de - light in its prom - ise makes the world so dear? There's a hush o - ver all;

2. O what charm, O what charm, has the night wrought to win me? I am held as by mag - ic or by fair - y art. There's a voice ring - ing low,

cres. *f*

Bright stars a-lone un-sleep-ing, Seem to stand on guard a-
It wakes my soul with-in me; Well I know its haunt-ing

Bright stars a-lone un-sleep-ing, Seem to stand on guard a-
It wakes my soul with-in me; Well I know its haunt-ing

rall. e dim.

bove me Al-lay-ing, al-lay-ing ev-'ry fear.
beau-ty! 'Tis ring-ing, 'tis ring-ing in my heart.

bove me Al-lay-ing, al-lay-ing ev-'ry fear.
beau-ty! 'Tis ring-ing, 'tis ring-ing in my heart.

Sunset

M. A. L. Lane

Con grazia

Pauline Meyer

mp

1. Soft and clear the sun-set light Gilds the shin-ing riv-er;
2. All the shad-ows, dark or dim, Mean that light is shin-ing;

1. Soft and clear the sun-set light Gilds the shin-ing riv-er;
2. All the shad-ows, dark or dim, Mean that light is shin-ing;

Swal - lows take their home-ward flight, Dart - ing wings a - quiv - er.
Ev - 'ry cloud of pearl - y rim Hath a sil - ver lin - ing.

Swal - lows take their home-ward flight, Dart - ing wings a - quiv - er.
Ev - 'ry cloud of pearl - y rim Hath a sil - ver lin - ing.

cres.   *mf*

On our ears no clam - or falls Save a dis - tant bell;
Are you bound by chains and bars, Where your soul doth dwell?

On our ears no clam - or falls Save a dis - tant bell;
Are you bound by chains and bars, Where your soul doth dwell?

f   *dim.*

Far a - cross the hills it calls "Hap - py day, fare - well!"
Ah! 'twill be a night of stars! Hap - py day, fare - well!

Far a - cross the hills it calls "Hap - py day, fare - well!"
Ah! 'twill be a night of stars! Hap - py day, fare - well!

The Spring is Coming

G. MacFarren

English Folk Song

1. The spring is com - ing re - solved to ban - ish The
2. The spring is com - ing to wake the ros - es, With

king of the ice with his tur - bu - lent train; With her
gay ser - e - nades from her chor - is - ter birds; Ev - 'ry

fair - y wand she bids them van - ish, And
breath - ing flow - ret's lip dis - clos - es A

wel - come the sun - shine to earth a - gain. Then
grat - i - tude sweet - er than mor - tal words, Shall

wel - come the sun - shine to earth a - gain.
grat - i - tude sweet - er than mor - tal words,

maid - ens fore - go the win - try kir - tle, And
we be the last to swell the meas - ure That

poco rit.

lace ev - 'ry bod - ice with bright green string, And
all Na - ture's chil - dren in har - mo - ny sing? Ah!

lace ev - 'ry bod - ice with bright green string, And
all Na - ture's chil - dren in har - mo - ny sing? Ah!

twine each lat - tice with wreaths of myr - tle To
no, we'll tune with a ho - li - er pleas - ure The

twine each lat - tice with wreaths of myr - tle To
no, we'll tune with a ho - li - er pleas - ure The

hon - or the ad - vent of joy - ful spring.
ca - rol of wel - come to joy - ful spring.

hon - or the ad - vent of joy - ful spring.
ca - rol of wel - come to joy - ful spring.

Cavalier Song

Henry Graham
Allegro moderato

Welsh Folk Tune

Com-rades, ride, for there's work to be done,

(ALTO)

Leagues to cov - er ere set of the sun, On we're gal - lop-ing,

on we're gal - lop - ing, on we're gal - lop-ing o - ver the road.

on we're gal - lop - ing, on we're gal - lop-ing o - ver the road.

1. Ear - ly this morn - ing the sum - mons came, Ride we in an - swer with
2. On - ward by wood-land and hill and down, On - ward thro' vil - lage and

1. Ear - ly this morn - ing the sum - mons came, Ride we in an - swer with
2. On - ward by wood-land and hill and down, On - ward thro' vil - lage and

hearts a - flame. Com - rades, ride, for there's work to be done,
mar - ket - town. Com - rades, ride, for there's work to be done,

hearts a - flame. Com - rades, ride, for there's work to be done,
mar - ket - town. Com - rades, ride, for there's work to be done,

Leagues to cov - er ere set of the sun, On we're gal - lop-ing,

Leagues to cov - er ere set of the sun, On we're gal - lop-ing,

on we're gal - lop - ing, On we're gal - lop- ing o - ver the road.

on we're gal - lop - ing, On we're gal - lop- ing o - ver the road.

Allan Shaw

Moderato   *mf*

Fair Cuba

Eduardo Sánchez de Fuentes
Arr. by Sewall Day

1. Fair   Cu - ba . . sits enthroned in an o - cean of light,
   chant - ing . . are her fields and her for - ests of green,
2. The   palm trees . bow in greet-ing, while soft breezes blow,
   coun - try . . and in cit - y wher-e'er voic-es rise,

Where the dawn comes in   splen - dor, . . . And the stars of the
And the glo - ry they   lend   her; . . . Of all trop - i - cal
And the cane - brakes are   sway - ing. . . . See the maize, row on
Hear the words they are   say - ing: . . . "We will praise our fair

night Shine with   ra - di - ance bright, Shine with   ra - di - ance bright.
isles, Fair - est Cu - ba   is queen, Fair - est Cu - ba   is queen!
row, All   its   tas - sels   a - glow, All   its   tas - sels   a - glow!
isle; Lift   her   name to   the skies, Lift   her   name to   the skies!"

En -
In

We greet thee, Cu - ba,   land of flow'rs and of song!
We greet thee, Cu - ba,   land of flow'rs and of song!

We greet thee, Cu - ba,   land of flow'rs and of song!
We greet thee, Cu - ba,   land of flow'rs and of song!

The hap - py birds a - wake   and thy prais - es pro -

The hap - py birds a - wake   and thy prais - es pro -

long, . . pro-long. O Isle of Cu - ba, how thy sweet, ten - der

long, . . pro-long. O Isle of Cu - ba, how thy sweet, ten - der

calm . . Heal-eth all wea - ry souls with its balm,

calm . . Heal-eth all wea - ry souls with its balm,

With its mag - i - cal balm. . . . We greet thee, . .

With its mag - i - cal balm. . . . We greet thee, . .

The Flowers' Lament

Joan Luther

Non troppo lento

French Folk Tune

1. Dark is the sky; the clouds are
2. Sum-mer has fled. We loved her

low - er - ing; Brown is the field and bare the hill;
fer - vent-ly; Loath were we all to say "Fare - well."

cres.

Drear - y the sound of wa - ters mur - m'ring, Held in a
Sad - ly we sigh, our fate be - moan - ing; Long-ing in

cres.

Drear - y the sound of wa - ters mur - m'ring, Held in a
Sad - ly we sigh, our fate be - moan - ing; Long-ing in

cres.

cres.

grasp aus - tere and chill. Where are the
vain with her to dwell! Yet in the

grasp aus - tere and chill. Where are the
vain with her to dwell! Yet in the

birds? the grove was mu - sic - al On - ly a few short
air a ten - der mel - o - dy, Chant - ed by view - less

birds? the grove was mu - sic - al On - ly a few short
air a ten - der mel - o - dy, Chant - ed by view - less

weeks a - go. Have we no friends— no loy - al
her - alds near, Bids us pre - pare for com - ing

weeks a - go. Have we no friends— no loy - al
her - alds near, Bids us pre - pare for com - ing

fol - low-ers, Read - y to brave the cold and snow?
hap - pi-ness; Tells us that spring will soon be here!

fol - low-ers, Read - y to brave the cold and snow?
hap - pi-ness; Tells us that spring will soon be here!

Morning Prayer

M. Louise Baum

Peter Tschaikowsky, Op. 39

Arr. from Op. 39 by H. S. LEAVITT

1. O God, we praise Thee, greet-ing the light. Thy love has
2. Ah, what the ser-vice pleas-eth Thee best? Wait we the

kept us, thro' all the long night. . . . Com-fort Thou send-est to
an-swer, held close to Thy breast, . . . "Love thou thy neigh-bor, and

kept us, thro' all the long night.   Com-fort Thou send-est to
an-swer, held close to Thy breast.   "Love thou thy neigh-bor, and

love and o - bey Thee, To   those   who   love, who love and o - bey!
peace li - eth near us, The   path   of   peace, of peace li - eth near!

To   those   who   love   and o - bey!
The   path   of   peace   li - eth near!

Oh, Where are Kings and Empires Now

Arthur C. Coxe   A. A. Wild

1. Oh, where   are kings and   em - pires now,   Of   old that went and
2. For   not   like king - doms   of   the world,   The   ho - ly church of

1. Oh, where   are kings and   em - pires now,   Of   old that went and
2. For   not   like king - doms   of   the world,   The   ho - ly church of

came? But Lord, Thy Church is pray-ing yet, A thou-sand years the
God! Though earth-quake shocks are threat'ning her, And tem-pests are a

came? But Lord, Thy Church is pray-ing yet, A thou-sand years the
God! Though earth-quake shocks are threat'ning her, And tem-pests are a-

same! . We mark her good-ly bat-tle-ments, And her foun-da-tions
broad; . Un-shak-en as e-ter-nal hills, Im-mov-a-ble she

same! . We mark her good-ly bat-tle-ments, And her foun-da-tions
broad; . Un-shak-en as e-ter-nal hills, Im-mov-a-ble she

strong: And hear with-in the sol-emn voice Of her un-end-ing song!
stands,—A moun-tain that shall fill the earth, A house not made by hands.

strong: And hear with-in the sol-emn voice Of her un-end-ing song!
stands,—A moun-tain that shall fill the earth, A house not made by hands.

On the Mountain

Celia Standish

Felix Mendelssohn
Arr. from Opus 64 by H. S. Leavitt

Sun, sun on the moun - tain, rising in splendor high, . . . Gild - ing the crags with glints of gold, And

flood-ing with light the morn - ing sky! Oh, sun, sun on the

Oh, sun, sun on the

moun - tain, ris - ing in splen - dor high, ...

moun - tain, ris - ing in splen - dor, splen - dor high,

splen - dor high, ...

light, And paint - ing a rain - bow a - gainst the far

light, And paint - ing a rain - bow a - gainst the far

height; . . . 'Tis the sign of a mor - - row bright.

height; It is the sign of a mor - - row bright.

height; It is the sign of a mor - - row bright.

Chorus of Pilgrims

Giuseppe Verdi

Arr. from the Opera " I Lombardi "

From a-far, gra-cious Lord, Thou didst

gath - er Thy flock, on these shores of the

o - - cean. Thee they owned as their God and their

Fa - ther; And when left . . . . . in the wild waste for -

Fa - ther; And when left . . . . in the wild waste for -

lorn,   Still they served Thee with stead - fast de -

lorn,

vo - - - tion. Hear the cry which their chil - dren are

send - ing. With the ac - cents of pen - i - tence

mp

With the ac - cents of pen - i - tence

mp

blend - ing. Save Thy peo - - - ple from per - il and

blend - ing. Save Thy peo - - - ple from per - il and

scorn.

scorn.   Oh,   let peace   bend . . . its arch of de -

dued,   our souls be subdued, our souls be sub-dued. . . . . .

dued,   our souls be subdued, our souls be sub-dued. . . . . .

Eldorado [1]

Frederick E. Weatherly

Ciro Pinsuti

Andante moderato

What ho! ye gray-beard mar - i - ners, Now whith - er do ye

sail? Your hearts are light, the skies are bright, And cheer - ly blows the

[1] Complete in the three upper voices

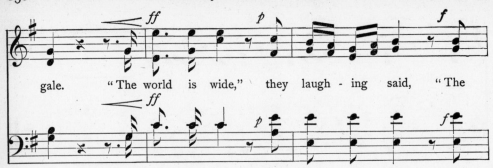

gale.   "The world is wide," they laugh - ing said,   "The

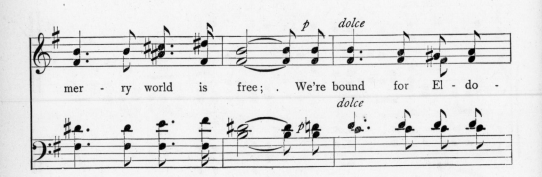

mer - ry world is free; . We're bound for El - do -

ra - do, A - cross the gold - en sea, We're bound for El - do -

ra - do, A - cross the gold - en sea!"   Thou

pale and lone-ly maid-en, Up-on the o-cean strand, Whom

seek - est thou with pa - tient brow? Why wav - est thou thy

hand? "The sum - mer comes, the sum - mer dies," The

maid - en an - swered low, "I wait for one who

cres.

sailed a-way These man-y years a-go!..   I

f Con anima   *dim. e rall.*   *p*   *molto rit.*

wait   for   one who sailed a-way These man-y   years a-

Poco meno mosso

go!"   Creep home, thou lone-ly maid-en, Creep home and sleep thy

Creep home, thou lone-ly maid-en,

rinforzando

sleep;   The fond-est hearts that ev-er lived Lie bur-ied   in the

deep. Come back, ye gray-beard mar - i - ners, Trust not the tempt - ing

gleam, The land of El - do - ra - do is but a po - et's

dream! a po - et's dream, a po - et's dream, a po - et's

Is but a po - et's dream! .

dream, ... Is but a po - et's dream! . .

PART IV
FOUR-PART SONGS AND CHORUSES
Whisper, Whisper!

Anonymous
Andante

Finnish Folk Tune

1. Whis-per, whis-per tales of spring From far dis-tant lands, .
2. Whis-per, whis-per tales of youth, When the heart beats high, .

While the o-cean mur-murs, mur-murs, O'er the gold-en sands. .
When the sol-emn pine trees mur-mur, While the clouds drift by. . .

Hark! the Summons

Traditional
Allegro

Welsh Folk Tune

1. Hark! the sum-mons, come, my . . fel-lows,
2. Shep-herds, quit your cares for . . pleas-ure,
3. Toil and trou-ble lie be-hind us,

Fa la la la la la la la la. Crown your hats with
Fa la la la la la la la la. Fish-ers, leave your
Fa la la la la la la la la. Think no more of

La la la la

hol ly . ber - ry, Fa la la la la la
nets and . wher - ry, Fa la la la la la
chanc - es . drea - ry, Fa la la la la la

La la la la

la la la. Hark! the peal - ing bells that tell us,
la la la. This must be a night of lei - sure,
la la la. While the well - known strains re - mind us,

Fa la la la la la la la la. 'Tis the eve of
La la la la

new year mer - ry, Fa la la la la la la la la.

Winds of November

Allan Shaw

M. Bellingham

Con spirito

1. Up the hills and down the vales Fast they fly,
2. Thro' the for-est bare they roam, Full of play,
3. Yet as win-ter draw-eth near, Hear them sigh,

fast they fly, Fill - ing now the i - dle
full of play, Driv - ing tim - id wood - folk
hear them sigh,— Van - ished joys are strange - ly

sails, And now rush - ing off to the sky. . .
home And fling - ing their treas - ure a - way. . .
dear— "O Sum - mer, fair Sum - mer, good - by!" . .

To the Heights

Joan Luther

Frederick Shaw

Moderato

mp

1. In the val - ley shad - ows length - en
2. Gird thy - self for high en - deav - or;

mp

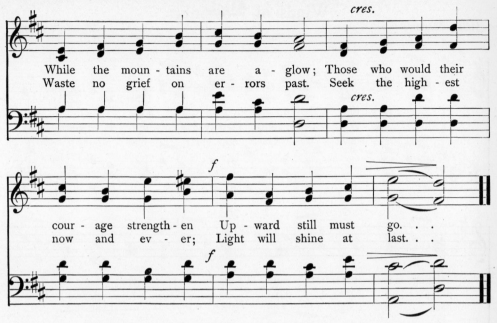

cres.

While the moun-tains are a - glow; Those who would their
Waste no grief on er - rors past. Seek the high - est

f

cour - age strength - en Up - ward still must go. . .
now and ev - er; Light will shine at last. . .

The Shuttle

M. A. L. Lane

F. Remsen

Allegretto

p

1. Back and forth the shut - tle flies, Hard - ly seen by care - less eyes';
2. Slow - ly does the pat - tern grow, Line by line its beau - ty show,

cres. *f* *dim.* *p*

Fly - ing, fly - ing, ev - er fly - ing; 'Tis of life the to - ken.
Wid - er, wid - er, ev - er wid - er Till the thread is bro - ken.

The Exile

Celia Standish

Frederick Shaw

1. The waves of old o-cean Are call-ing to me! They bring me a mes-sage From far o'er the sea. Where proud hills of my own land Look out o'er the blue. Oh, green hills, oh fair skies! I come back to you.

2. Oh land of my fa-thers, Thy dear voice I hear. And far o'er the o-cean 'Tis whis-per-ing clear. Thro' ex-ile and thro' sor-row My heart still is true. Oh, green hills, oh fair skies! I come back to you.

The Garden by the Sea

M. A. L. Lane

Moderato con grazia

Ludwig van Beethoven

Arranged from " Minuet "

1. From a land that lies be - yond the sea, Far a -
2. "We will wait," the gar - den ros - es say, "Till you

way, far a - way! Comes a sweet but fleet - ing dream to
come, till you come"; Say the dah - lias clad in col - ors

me, When all else is gray. There's a
gay, "We'll wel - come you home." While each

gar - den where in hap - py hours, Long a - go, long a -
rip - pling wave in ebb and flow O'er the sea, o'er the

go,　I have played a - lone a - mong the flow'rs　And
sea,　Seems to whis - per ver - y soft and low,　"O .

heard sea . winds blow.　In . vain do I sigh; till . .
come back to . me!"　In . vain do they call; my . .

liv - ing is . o'er　I must long for that en - chant - ed
child - hood is . o'er;　Though the sea will beat up - on that

shore　Ev - er - more,　ev - er - more!　more!
shore　Ev - er - more,　ev - er - more!　more!

Consolation[1]

M. Louise Baum

Franz Schubert
Arranged from Op. 15

1. Now o'er the sleep - ing world, Night draws nigh; Sol - emn and
2. Earth has no rest - ing place, Knows no peace, Wea - ry the

si - lent the earth doth lie.
toil till it find sur - cease.

Now o'er the sleep - ing world,
Earth has no rest - ing place,

[1] Complete in three upper voices

Night draws nigh; Sol - emn and si - lent the earth doth
Knows no peace, Wea - ry the toil till it find sur -

lie.   Voic - es of long a - go Are sound-ing
cease.   Yet to the heart of faith Soft voic - es

near ; And wak - en sweet mem - o - ries,
call ; The fu - ture out - shines the past,

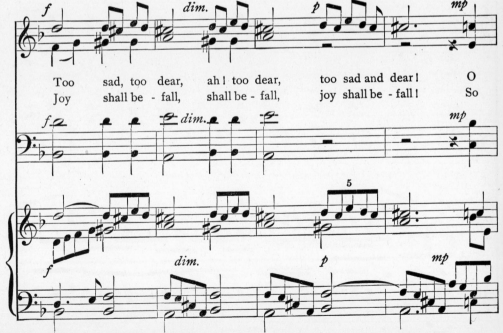

Too sad, too dear, ah! too dear, too sad and dear! O
Joy shall be - fall, shall be - fall, joy shall be - fall! So

days that were sum - mer fair, All gold - en
lov - ing what once was sweet, Heav'n smiles more

bright, With youth's ten - der beau - ty a -
fair, All beau - ty and won - der are

light!
there!

Why must ye pale and fade?
Pour - ing on all who weep

Why de - part? Leav - ing no spring to re - new the heart?
Com - fort's spell, Love whis-pers smil - ing, "All's well, all's well."

Loch Lomond [1]

Scotch Folk Song

Moderato
mf

1. By yon bon-nie banks and yon bon-nie braes, Where the
2. I mind where we part-ed in yon shad-y glen, On the
3. The wee bird-ies sing and the wild flow-ers spring; And in

sun shines bright on Loch Lo - mond; Oh,
steep, steep side of Loch Lo - mond; Where in
sun-shine, the wa-ters are sleep-ing; But the

we twa ha'e pass'd sa mon-y blithe-some days, On the
pur-ple hue, the High-land hills we view, And the
bro-ken heart, it seeks no sec-ond spring, And the

bon-nie, bon-nie banks of Loch Lo - mond. Oh!
morn shines out from the gloam - ing. Oh!
world knows not how we're greet - ing. Oh!

[1] Complete in three upper voices

Hymn of Freedom

Celia Standish
Andante Maestoso

Gaetano Donizetti
Arr. from the grand opera " Il Poliuto "

1. Sing of our free land, Firm in its might, Strong in its own . truth, Oh, still it guards the right. . God of Na - tions, God of Na - tions, Praise to Thee, to Thee who made us free. Home of the home - less Oh, may you ev - er be. . .

2. Far o'er the o - cean Comes a great host, Seek - ing our home - land, Our prai - ries and our coast. . God of Na - tions, God of Na - tions, Praise to Thee, to Thee who made us free. Sing of our free - land, Oh, still it guards the right. .

The Owl

Estelle Cushman

Estelle Cushman

Pensieroso

1. A big brown owl lives in the wood, Qui-et-ly as a
2. O'er-head the moon's soft sil-v'ry light Lends new beau-ty

cres.   dim. e rit.

big owl should, The whole day through, The whole day
to the night. The trees soft-ly sigh, The trees soft-ly

a tempo
mf

through. But when at night I try to sleep, A
sigh. But hark! the owl a-gain I hear! More

dim.

lone-ly watch that owl must keep. And I can hear the
soft-ly now, yet faint and clear. I think he must be

whole night thro', His mourn-ful ques-tion "O, who are you? O
sleep-y, too. 'Tis now a whis-per, "O, who are you? O

who— who— who are you?   O who?"
who— who— who are you?   O who?"

O who? O who?
O who? O who?

On Venice Waters

Henry Vaughan
Andantino

Otto Roeder
Arranged

1. 'Tis night on Ven-ice wa-ters,   And
2. Far off in gold-en splen-dor   The

o'er the calm la-goon A gon - do - la is
sun goes down to rest, The lights of dis - tant

glid - ing Be - neath the mel - low moon. The
Ven - ice Shine o'er the wa - ter's breast. O

gon - do - lier is row - ing, His love is by his
gold - en hour of twi - light, O hap - py time of

side,   His eyes are bright with a glad love - light And he
love,   When the joy - ous song   is borne a - long To the

REFRAIN

O - ver the foam we

sings as they stem the tide.
sweet sum-mer stars a - bove.

Un-der the dream-y

glide . . . Borne on the rip-pling tide, . . . Un - der

Un-der the dream - y

sum - mer skies, Watch-ing the mist a - round us rise. . .

What tho' the world be wide, . . . Love's gold - en star will

guide, . . . Drift - ing a - long, Glad is our song,

While we are side by side, . . While we are side by side, . .

While we are side by side. . . .

accelerando

To the Hermit Thrush

English version by M. Louise Baum

F. Paolo Tosti
Arr. from "La Serenata"

1. Flow then, O voice of mu - - sic, The
2. Flow then, O voice of mu - - sic, The

twi - light hours a - wait thee; The
lone - ly stars will hear thee; The

eve-ning air to rap-ture shall e-late thee,
sing-ing stream will make an ech-o near thee,

Hearts all in joy will mate thee;
Now plain-tive, now to cheer thee;

Flow   on, O voice of mu - - sic,
Flow   on, thou voice of mu - - sic,

Flow   on, O voice of mu - sic!
Flow   on, thou voice of mu - sic!

Soon   the   moon - light in splen - - dor,
Lulled   by   breez - es that love   them,

Wings   of   the dark   will   sil - - ver;
Waves   are a - sleep   out   yon - - der,

Sweet - ly thy ves - per hymn with sleep will dim All
All things are still, in - deed, thy song to heed, That

eyes to dream - ing ten - der.
charms the night a - bove them.

Dim all to dream-ing ten - - der,
Ah! charm the night a - bove them,

Dim all to dream-ing ten - - der,
Ah! charm the night a - bove them,

Flow,　thou　voice　of　mu　-　-　sic,

Flow,　thou　voice　of　mu　-　-　sic,

Flow,　thou　voice　of　mu　-　-　sic,

Flow,　thou　voice　of　mu　-　-　sic,

Flow . . . . . .   on !
Flow . . . . . .   on !

Ah ! . . . .   la, ...

Old Folks at Home [1]

Stephen C. Foster   Stephen C. Foster

Moderato espress.

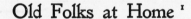

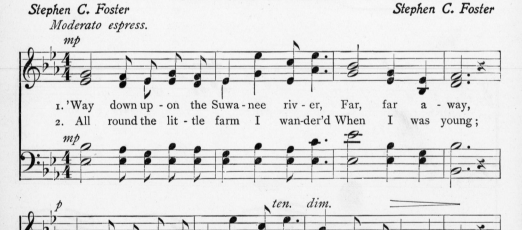

1. 'Way   down up - on the Suwa - nee   riv - er,   Far,   far   a - way,
2. All   round the lit - tle farm I   wan-der'd When   I   was young;

There's where my heart is turn - ing   ev - er.There's where the old folks stay.
Then man - y   hap - py days I squan-der'd,Man - y   the songs I   sung.

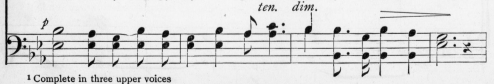

Piu p

All up and down the whole cre - a - tion, Sad - ly I roam,
When I was play - ing with my broth - er, Hap - py was I,

Still long-ing for the old plan - ta - tion, And for the old folks at home.
Oh, take me to my kind old moth - er, There let me live and die.

All the world is sad and drear - y, Ev - 'ry where I roam,

Oh! how my heart grows sad and wea - ry, Far from the old folks at home.

What Have We Done To-day?

Nixon Waterman

Arthur B. Targett

mp Andante cantabile

1. We shall do so much in the years to come, But
2. We shall be so kind in the aft-er-while, But
3. We shall reap such joys in the by-and-by, But

Uh . . . .

what have we done to-day? We shall give our gold in a
what have we been to-day? We shall bring each lone-ly
what have we sown to-day? We shall build us man-sions

what have we done to-day?
what have we been to-day?
what have we sown to-day?

Uh . . . .

prince - ly sum, But what did we give to - day? We shall
life a smile, But what have we brought to - day? We shall
in the sky But what have we built to - day? 'Tis

What did we give to - day? . .
What have we brought to - day? . .
What have we built to - day? . .

lift the heart and dry the tear,
give to truth a grand - er birth,
sweet in i - dle dreams to bask,

We shall plant a hope in .
And to stead - fast faith a . .
But . here and now do we

We shall speak the . . words of
We shall feed the . . hung'-ring
Yes, . . this is the thing our

place of fear. We shall speak the . . words of
deep - er worth. We shall feed the . . hung - 'ring
do our task? Yes, . . this is the thing our

love and cheer, But what have we done to - day?
souls of earth, But whom have we fed to - day?
souls must ask, What have we done to - day?

love and cheer, What have we done . . to - day?
souls of earth, Whom have we fed . . . to - day?
souls must ask, What have we done . . to - day?

O Sea, How Fair Art Thou[1]

H. Weidt

Andante espressivo

1. O, by thy side I'm hap-py When day is al-most gone, And
2. O, Sea, how wide the vi-sion That o-pens to my sight, When

sun-set's gold-en ar-go-sies Are float-ing smooth-ly on; Thy
ten-der twi-light soft-ly draws The cur-tain of the night! The

waves .. are creep-ing o'er the sand, Thy breath is on my
troub-ling world slips far a-way, Thy glo-ry fills me

poco animato e cres.

brow; My joy-ful heart is sing-ing, My joy-ful heart is
now; My joy-ful heart is sing-ing, My joy-ful heart is

poco animato e cres.

[1] **Complete in three upper voices**

singing, How fair, O Sea, how fair . . art thou! How fair, how fair, how fair . . . art thou!

singing, How fair, O Sea, how fair . . art thou! How fair, how fair, how fair . . . art thou!

The Stormy Petrel

M. A. L. Lane

Wilson White

Grazioso

1. Like a swal - low, fly - ing low, Like a sea - gull, on the wave, Thou hast man - y miles to go,
2. Lit - tle com - rade, weak and small, Thou hast crossed the track - less sea; Thou hast dared ad - ven - ture all;

But thy heart is brave. . A stran - ger on our
Can such cour - age be? . . The an - gry winds may

shore, . Thou hast paused to rest; . . Wilt thou come to
cry; . . Thou art not a - fraid; . . Clouds may dark - en

us no more, Thou rare but ev - er wel - come guest?
all thy sky, But thy stout heart is not dis - mayed;

Wilt thou come to us no more, Thou ev - er wel-come guest?
Clouds may dark - en all thy sky, But thou art not dis - mayed.

The Old Oaken Bucket

Samuel Woodworth   E. Kaillmark

Colla voce pp

1, 2 and 3. Oak — en buck — et, iron — bound

pp

1. How dear to this heart are the scenes of my
2. The moss - cov - ered buck - et I hailed as a
3. How sweet from the green moss - y brim to re -

mf

dim.

buck - et, The moss - cov - ered buck — et in the

dim.

child - hood, When fond rec - ol - lec - tion pre - sents them to
treas - ure, For of - ten at noon, when re - turned from the
ceive it, As, poised on the curb, it in - clined to my

pp

well. Oak — en buck - et, iron — bound

pp

view! The or - chard, the mead - ow, the deep tan - gled
field, I found it the source of an ex - qui - site
lips! Not a full blush - ing gob - let could tempt me to

mf

buck - et, The moss - cov - ered buck - et in the well.

wild - wood, And ev - 'ry loved spot which my in - fan - cy knew;
pleas - ure, The pur - est and sweet - est that na - ture can yield.
leave it, Tho' filled with the nec - tar that Ju - pi - ter sips.

p dolce leggiero

The wide - spread - ing pond, and the mill that stood by it, The
How ar - dent I seized it, with hands that were glow - ing, And
And now, far re - moved from the loved hab - i - ta - tion, The

The wide - spread - ing pond, and the mill that stood by it, The
How ar - dent I seized it, with hands that were glow - ing, And
And now, far re - moved from the loved hab - i - ta - tion, The

bridge and the rock where the cat - a - ract fell; The
quick to the white peb - bled bot - tom it fell, Then
tear of re - gret will in - tru - sive - ly swell, As

bridge and the rock where the cat - a - ract fell; The
quick to the white peb - bled bot - tom it fell, Then
tear of re - gret will in - tru - sive - ly swell, As

cot of my fa - ther, the dai - ry - house nigh it, And
soon, with the em - blem of truth o - ver - flow - ing, And
fan - cy re - verts to my fa - ther's plan - ta - tion, And

cot of my fa - ther, the dai - ry - house nigh it, And
soon, with the em - blem of truth o - ver - flow - ing, And
fan - cy re - verts to my fa - ther's plan - ta - tion, And

cres.

e'en the rude buck - et that hung in the well.
drip - ping with cool - ness, it rose from the well.
sighs for the buck - et that hung in the well.

cres.

e'en the rude buck - et that hung in the well. The
drip - ping with cool - ness, it rose from the well. The
sighs for the buck - et that hung in the well. The

cres.

pp

1,2,3. Oak - en buck - et, iron - bound buck - et,

pp

old oak - en buck - et, the i - ron-bound buck - et, The
old oak - en buck - et, the i - ron-bound buck - et, The
old oak - en buck - et, the i - ron-bound buck - et, The

mf

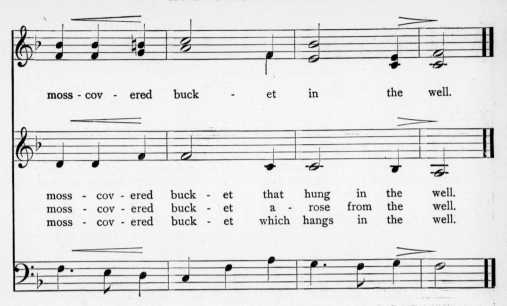

moss - cov - ered buck — et in the well.

moss - cov - ered buck - et that hung in the well.
moss - cov - ered buck - et a - rose from the well.
moss - cov - ered buck - et which hangs in the well.

Fair October

Allan Harvey

L. S. Wilson

The field;
Oh, far!

Glow with the
Gold is the

The field;
Oh, far!

Glow with the
Gold is the

1. The wood and field, . . . the coun - try side,
2. Oh, near and far . . . the way - side flames!

col - ors   of   the   rai - ment   of   kings. .
trib - ute   of   the   year   to   the   frost. . .

col - ors   of   the   rai - ment   of   kings. .
trib - ute   of   the   year   to   the   frost. .

mp

Of   kings. .   Each hedge and
The   frost. .   Rich hoard of

p   cres.

Each   copse;   Su - perb   Oc -
Of   wealth;   Em - 'ralds   and

p   cres.

Each   copse;   Su - perb   Oc -
Of   wealth;   Em - 'ralds   and

cres.

copse . . . . is   pur - ple - dyed. .
wealth . . . . the   au - tumn   claims.

f

to - ber   wide   her   boun - ty   flings—
ru - bies—   not   a   jew - el   lost—

f

to - ber   wide   her   boun - ty   flings—
ru - bies—   not   a   jew - el   lost—

f   p

And   wide   her   boun - ty   flings—   The   wild birds
And   not   a   jew - el   lost—   No   rose - bud

They call,
Where, gleam-ing
No hue,
In end-less

They call,
No hue,

call ... from tree and moun-tain wall
hue ... but na-ture's deep-est blue

bright, ... gay hues the eye in-vite; Their ra-diant
chain ... a-dorns the dew-y plain. Au-tum-nal

So bright,
Their ra-diant
In chain,
Au-tum-nal

glo-ry weaves a charm o'er all. Oh, hail thou pag-eant of de-light!
splen-dors hill and vale im-bue, For fair Oc-to-ber now doth reign.

glo-ry weaves a charm o'er all. Oh, hail thou pag-eant of de-light!
splen-dors hill and vale im-bue, For fair Oc-to-ber now doth reign.

Spirit of Peace [1]

M. A. L. Lane

Ludwig Van Beethoven
Arr. from op. 97 by Sewall Day

Andante cantabile
p dolce

1. Heark - en,   O   Spir - it,   we   ask   thine   aid,   thy   pro -
2. Spir - it,   be - lov - ed,   there   is   no   com - fort   with -

in times of
are found where

tec - tion,   In   times   of   tri - umph   and   joy,   in   times   of
out   thee,   For   wretch - ed   ter - ror   and   pain   be - long   to

in times of
are found where

1 Complete in three upper voices

fail - ure and grief!
war has its will.

fail - ure and sor - row! O keep us from an - ger, Let not thy
war's grim tra - di - tion! Our pride needs re - buk - ing; We are but

fail - ure and grief!
war has its will.

pa - tience for - sake us, Be thou in dark - ness our
chil - dren be - fore thee, O keep our hearts from the

In days of stress our re - lief!
And from the wish - ing of ill!

light,   our bless-ed hope for the mor - row!   Strong- est   are
shame   of an un - wor - thy am - bi - tion!   Strong- est   are

In days of stress our re - lief!
And from the wish - ing of ill!

cres.

they   who can with - stand all   de - fi - ance; So may we
they   who can with - stand all   de - fi - ance; So may we

cres.

cres.

strive   to   ush - er   in   thy   reign   of   love,   thy
strive   to   ush - er   in   thy   reign   of   love,   thy

reign   of   love   a - mong   us.   So   may   we   strive   to   ush - er
reign   of   love   a - mong   us.   So   may   we   strive   to   ush - er
So   may   we
So   may   we

in thy reign of love, thy reign of love a - mong us.
in thy reign of love, thy reign of love a - mong us.

Thou Art Near Me, Margarita [1]

Erik Meyer-Helmund
Arranged

1. When the waves are gen - tly flow - ing,
2. When the rug - ged cliff de - scend - ing,

In the eve - ning red all glow - ing, When the day is
To strange lands my way I'm bend - ing, White the sea - foam

[1] Complete in three upper voices

ritard molto

slow - ly dy - ing, When a - far sweet bells are sigh - ing;
plays be - fore me, Through my soul a dream comes o'er me;

ritard molto

a tempo

Thou .. art near . me, Mar - ga - ri - ta!
Thou .. art near . me, Mar - ga - ri - ta!

a tempo

Thou .. art near me, Mar - ga - ri - ta!
Thou .. art near me, Mar - ga - ri - ta!

Thou .. art near . me, Mar - ga - ri - ta!
Thou .. art near . me, Mar - ga - ri - ta!

Thou . art near me, Mar - ga - ri - - - ta!
Thou . art near me, Mar - ga - ri - - - ta!

Lovely Spring[1]

Willem Coenen
Arranged

Andante

1. When the spring . . . has climbed the
2. Was it not . . . in spring, thou

[1] Complete in three upper voices

moun - tain's height, When be - neath . . the bright sun
dear - est maid, That thy heart . . re-veal'd it - -

melts . . the snow, When the first green leaf comes
self . . . to mine, That thy lips to me the

mead - - - ows show, . When on
ev - - - - er thine. . In the

agitato

hill . . . . and plain Ends old win - ter's reign, And the
shad - y grove, From the boughs . . a - bove, How the

agitato
p

earth . . . re - vives   from   ling -   'ring pain,   Loud   I
birds . . pour'd down   their   notes . . . of love!   Loud   I

hear   a   voice   Through the wel   - kin   ring,   through the
hear   a   voice   Through the wel   - kin   ring,   through the

all . . re - joice !   Wel - come, love - ly Spring,   wel - come,

love - - ly   spring ! . .

spring! . Mor - tals all re - joice! . Wel-come,

love - - - ly spring! . .

Bugle Song

Alfred Tennyson   *Henry Hadley*

The splen-dor falls on cas-tle walls And

snow-y sum-mits old in sto-ry; The long light shakes a-

And the wild, ...

cross the lakes,   And the wild, . wild .

And the

cat-a-ract leaps in glo - ry.   Blow, bu-gle, blow,

Blow, bu-gle,

Blow, bu - gle, blow, ... Set the wild ech - oes fly - ing!

Blow, bu - gle, blow,

blow,

Blow, bu - gle, blow, Blow, bu - gle, blow, ...

Blow, bu - gle, blow,

Blow, bu - gle, blow,

An - swer, ech - oes, an - swer, ech - oes, dy - ing, . .

dy - ing,

dy - - - - - ing. O hark, ...

dy - - ing. O hark! . . . . And

dy - - ing. how thin . . . . .

dy - ing. and clear,

thin - ner,   clear - er,   far - ther go - ing! O sweet   and far   from

cliff and scar The   horns of   elf - land faint - ly,   faint - ly   blow - ing!

Blow, ...
Blow, . . .   Let us hear   the   pur - ple glens re - ply - ing,
Blow, . .
Blow,

An - swer,   ech - oes,
Blow, bu - gle, blow,   Blow, bu - gle, blow,
An - swer,   ech - oes,
Blow, bu - gle, blow, . .

dy - ing, dy - ing, dy - ing. O love, they die in

yon rich sky, They faint on hill or field or riv - er; Our

ech - oes roll from soul to soul, And grow for - ev - er and for -

ev - er. Blow, bu - gle, blow, Blow, bu - gle, blow, . . .
Blow, bu - gle,

Blow, bu - gle, blow.

blow, set the wild ech-oes fly - ing. Blow, bu gle,

blow, Blow, bu - gle, blow, ... An - swer, ech - oes,
Blow, bu - gle, blow,

Blow, bu - gle, blow, dy - - - ing.

an - swer, ech - oes, dy - ing, . . dy - ing.
dy - ing.

dy - ing, dy - ing.

Night and Day

Robert Louis Stevenson. Arr.   Earl Towner

Andante con Moto

When the day is done, Through the
Ev - 'ry path and plot, Bush of

When the gold - en day is done, Through the clos - ing
Ev - 'ry path and ev - 'ry plot, Ev - 'ry bush of

p

Till the day be - gins, East . . . a -

p

Till at last the day be - gins In the east a -

mp

cres.

break - ing, Hedg - es and the whins

cres.

break - ing, In the hedg - es and the whins

cres.

dim.

Birds a - wak - ing. There my gar - den

dim.

Sleep - ing birds a - wak - ing. There my gar - den

dim.

grows a - gain, Green and ros - y paint - ed, . .

grows a - gain, Green and ros - y paint - ed,

As   at   eve   be - hind   the   pane

As   at   eve   be - hind   the   pane

From   my   eyes   it   faint - - - ed.

From   my   eyes   it   faint - - - ed.

FOUR-PART SONGS FOR BOY'S VOICES

Sweet and Low

Alfred Tennyson

Joseph Barnby

Larghetto

1st Tenor

1. Sweet and low, sweet and low, Wind of the west - ern sea;
2. Sleep and rest, sleep and rest, Fa - ther will come to thee soon;

2nd Tenor

1. Sweet and low, sweet and low, Wind of the west - ern sea;
2. Sleep and rest, sleep and rest, Fa - ther will come to thee soon;

1st Bass

1. Sweet and low, sweet and low, Wind of the west - ern sea;
2. Sleep and rest, sleep and rest, Fa - ther will come to thee soon;

2nd Bass

Low, low, . . breathe and blow, Wind of the west - ern
Rest, rest on moth - er's breast, Fa - ther will come to thee

Low, low, . . breathe and blow, Wind of the west - ern
Rest, rest on moth - er's breast, Fa - ther will come to thee

Low, low, . . breathe and blow, Wind of the west - ern
Rest, rest on moth - er's breast, Fa - ther will come to thee

sea; . O-ver the roll-ing wa-ters go,
soon; . Fa-ther will come to his babe in the nest,

sea; . O- -ver the wa-ters go,
soon; . Fa- -ther will come to the nest,

sea; . O-ver the roll-ing wa-ters go, . .
soon; . Fa-ther will come to his babe in the nest, . .

Come from the dy-ing moon and blow, Blow him a-gain to me, .
Sil-ver sails all out of the west, Un-der the sil-ver moon,

Come . . from the moon and blow, Blow him a-gain to me, .
Sil-ver sails out of the west, Un-der the sil-ver moon,

Come from the dy-ing moon and blow, Blow him a-gain to me, .
Sil-ver sails all out of the west, Un-der the sil-ver moon,

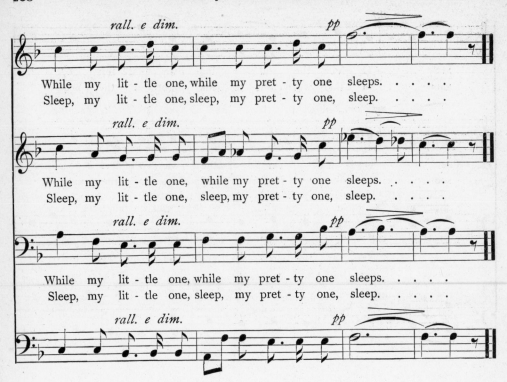

While my lit - tle one, while my pret - ty one sleeps. . . . .
Sleep, my lit - tle one, sleep, my pret - ty one, sleep. . . . .

While my lit - tle one, while my pret - ty one sleeps. . . . .
Sleep, my lit - tle one, sleep, my pret - ty one, sleep. . . . .

While my lit - tle one, while my pret - ty one sleeps. . . . .
Sleep, my lit - tle one, sleep, my pret - ty one, sleep. . . . .

There's Music in the Air

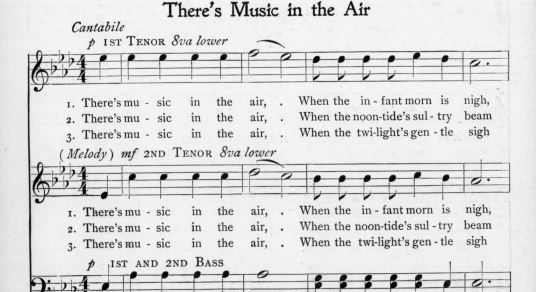

1. There's mu - sic in the air, . When the in - fant morn is nigh,
2. There's mu - sic in the air, . When the noon-tide's sul - try beam
3. There's mu - sic in the air, . When the twi-light's gen - tle sigh

1. There's mu - sic in the air, . When the in - fant morn is nigh,
2. There's mu - sic in the air, . When the noon-tide's sul - try beam
3. There's mu - sic in the air, . When the twi-light's gen - tle sigh

And faint its blush is seen . On the bright and laugh-ing sky.
Re - flects a gold - en light . On the dis - tant moun-tain stream.
Is lost on ev - 'ning's breast, As its pen - sive beau-ties die ;

And faint its blush is seen . On the bright and laugh-ing sky.
Re - flects a gold - en light . On the dis - tant moun-tain stream.
Is lost on ev - 'ning's breast, As its pen - sive beau-ties die ;

Many a harp's ec - stat - ic sound Thrills us with its joy pro - found,
When be - neath some grate-ful shade Sor-row's ach - ing head is laid,
Then, O then, the loved ones gone Wake the pure ce - les - tial song ; An -

Many a harp's ecs - tat - ic sound Thrills us with its joy pro - found,
When be - neath some grate-ful shade Sor-row's ach - ing head is laid,
Then, O then, the loved ones gone Wake the pure ce - les - tial song ; An -

(*Melody*)

While we list, en - chant - ed there, To the mu - sic in the air.
Sweet - ly to the spir - it there Comes the mu - sic in the air.
gel - ic voic - es greet us there, In the mu - sic in the air.

While we list, en - chant - ed there, To the mu - sic in the air.
Sweet - ly to the spir - it there Comes the mu - sic in the air.
gel - ic voic - es greet us there, In the mu - sic in the air.

We Meet Again To-night[1]

Con anima

IST AND 2ND Tenor *8va lower*

1. We meet a - gain to - night, boys, with mirth and song;
2. Where hand to hand its greet - ing so kind - ly gives,

mf IST AND 2ND Bass

mel - o - dy flow, ... Wher - ev - er we go, ...

Let mel - o - dy flow, Wher -
Let mel - o - dy flow, Wher -

1 Used by permission of S. Brainard's Sons Co.

ev - er we go, We dwell in friend - ship, ev - er so
ev - er we go, Where hope is nev - er dy - ing, and

true and strong, And sor - row nev - er know. . . . . .
friend - ship lives, True hearts will ev - er know. . . . . .

mp
We'll laugh and sing, and mer - ry be, and mer - ry be, to -
mp
We'll laugh . . . and sing . . . and mer - ry be, to -

night, my boys, We'll laugh and sing, and mer - ry be, and
night, . . . With nev - er a sor - row near, boys,

mer - ry be, to - night; . We'll laugh and sing, and

nev - er a fall - ing tear; . We'll laugh . . . . and

mer - ry be, and mer - ry be, to - night, my boys, And

sing, ... and mer - ry be to - night, . . . With

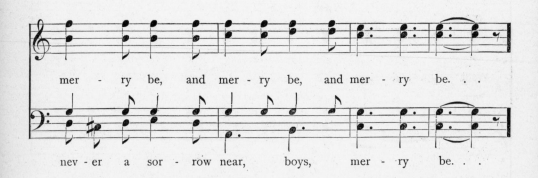

mer - ry be, and mer - ry be, and mer - ry be. . .

nev - er a sor - row near, boys, mer - ry be. . .

f After second stanza *rit.*

Wel - come the time, my boys, . we meet a - gain. .

f *rit.*

Tenting on the Old Camp Ground

Walter Kittredge

Walter Kittredge

Tempo di marcia

1. We're tent - ing to - night on the old camp ground,
2. We've been tent - ing to - night on the old camp ground,
3. We're tired . of war on the old camp ground,
4. We've been fight - ing to - day on the old camp ground,

Give us a song to cheer Our . wea - ry hearts, a
Think - ing of days gone by, Of the loved ones at home that
Man - y are dead and gone, Of the brave and true who've
Man - y are ly - ing near; Some are dead and

Give us a song to cheer
Think - ing . of days gone by,
Man - y are dead and gone,
Man - y are ly - ing near;

song of home And friends we love so dear.
gave us the hand, And the tear that said "good - bye."
left their homes, Oth - ers been wound - ed long.
some are dy - ing Ma - ny are in tears.

And friends we love so dear.
And the tear that said "good - bye."
Oth - ers been wound - ed long.
Ma - ny are in tears.

CHORUS

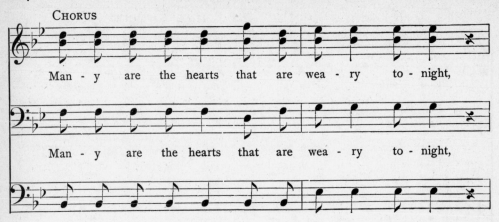

Man - y are the hearts that are wea - ry to - night,

Man - y are the hearts that are wea - ry to - night,

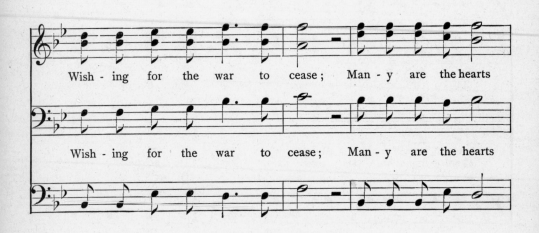

Wish - ing for the war to cease; Man - y are the hearts

Wish - ing for the war to cease; Man - y are the hearts

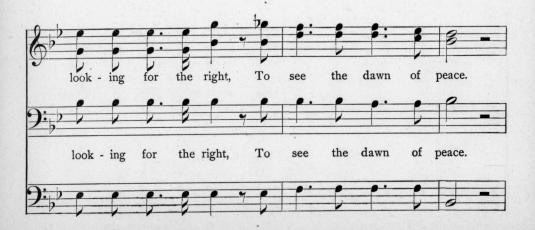

look - ing for the right, To see the dawn of peace.

look - ing for the right, To see the dawn of peace.

1, 2, 3

p
Tent - ing to - night, Tent - ing to - night,

p
Tent - ing to - night, Tent - ing to - night,

p

4 p
Tent - ing on the old camp ground. Dy - ing to - night,

p
Tent - ing on the old camp ground. Dy - ing to - night,

p

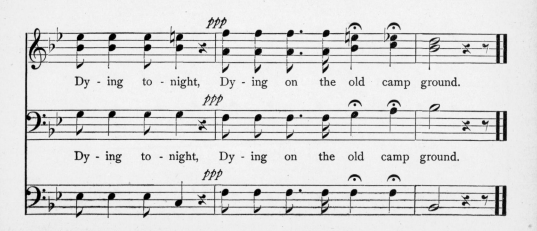

ppp
Dy - ing to - night, Dy - ing on the old camp ground.

ppp
Dy - ing to - night, Dy - ing on the old camp ground.

ppp

PART V

HYMNS AND PATRIOTIC SONGS

Regent Square

John Keble

Henry Smart

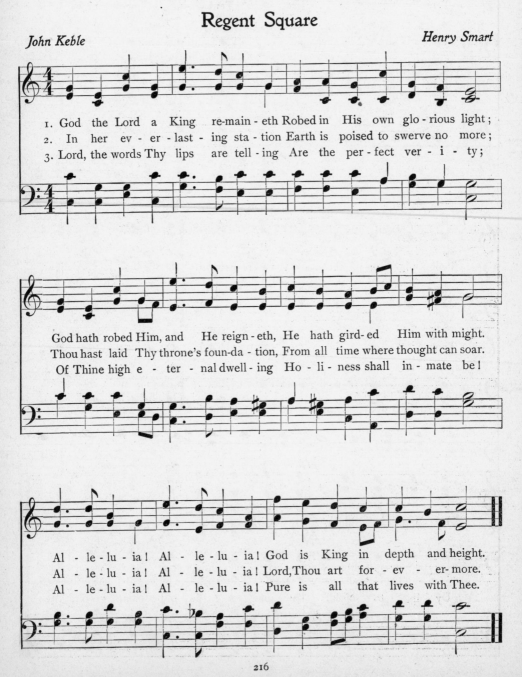

1. God the Lord a King re - main - eth Robed in His own glo - rious light;
2. In her ev - er - last - ing sta - tion Earth is poised to swerve no more;
3. Lord, the words Thy lips are tell - ing Are the per - fect ver - i - ty;

God hath robed Him, and He reign - eth, He hath gird - ed Him with might.
Thou hast laid Thy throne's foun - da - tion, From all time where thought can soar.
Of Thine high e - ter - nal dwell - ing Ho - li - ness shall in - mate be!

Al - le - lu - ia! Al - le - lu - ia! God is King in depth and height.
Al - le - lu - ia! Al - le - lu - ia! Lord, Thou art for - ev - er - more.
Al - le - lu - ia! Al - le - lu - ia! Pure is all that lives with Thee.

Aurelia

Edward H. Bickersteth   *Samuel S. Wesley*

1. O God, the Rock of a - ges, Who ev - er - more hast been, What
2. Our years are like the shad - ows O'er sun - ny hills that fly, Or
3. O Thou, who canst not slum - ber, Whose light grows nev - er pale, Teach

time the tem - pest rag - es, Our dwell - ing place se - rene; Be -
grass - es in the mead - ows That blos - som but to die; A
us a - right to num - ber Our years be - fore they fail. On

fore Thy first cre - a - tions, O Lord, the same as now, To
sleep, a dream, a sto - ry By stran - gers quick - ly told, An
us Thy mer - cy light - en, On us Thy good - ness rest; And

end - less gen - er - a - tions The ev - er - last - ing Thou!
un - re - main - ing glo - ry Of things that soon are old!
let Thy spir - it bright - en The heart Thy - self hath blessed.

cord our part-ing hymn of praise; We stand to bless Thee ere our
gan, with Thee shall end the day; Guard Thou the lips from sin, the
us its dark-ness in-to light; From harm and dan-ger keep Thy
sor-row, and our stay in strife; Then, when Thy voice shall bid our

wor-ship cease; Then, low-ly kneel-ing, wait Thy word of peace.
hearts from shame, That in this house have called up-on Thy name.
chil-dren free, For dark and light are both a-like to Thee.
con-flict cease, Call us, O Lord, to Thine e-ter-nal peace.

Guidance

Sabine Baring-Gould

Joseph Barnby

1. Now the day is o - ver, Night is draw-ing nigh; . .
2. Fa - ther, give the wea - ry Calm and sweet re - pose; . .
3. When the morn - ing wak - ens, Then may I a - rise . .

Shad - ows of the eve - ning Steal a-cross the sky.
With Thy ten-d'rest bless - ing May our eye-lids close.
Pure and fresh, and sin - less In Thy ho - ly eyes.

eve - ning Steal a - cross . . . . the sky.
bless - ing May our eye - - lids close.
sin - less In Thy ho - - ly eyes.

Portuguese Hymn

R. Keene   *Essay on Plain Chant*

1. How firm a foun-da-tion, ye saints of the Lord, Is laid for your
2. Fear not, I am with thee, oh, be not dis-mayed, For I am thy
3. When thro' the deep wa-ters I call thee to go, The riv-ers of
4. When thro' fier-y tri-als thy path-way shall lie, My grace, all suf-

faith in His ex-cel-lent Word! What more can He say than to
God, and will still give thee aid; I'll strength-en thee, help thee, and
sor-row shall not o-ver-flow; For I will be with thee, thy
fi-cient, shall be thy sup-ply; The flame shall not hurt thee; I

you He hath said, . Who un-to the Sav-iour for ref-uge have
cause thee to stand, . Up-held by My right-eous, Om-ni-po-tent
trou-bles to bless, . And sanc-ti-fy to thee thy deep-est dis-
on-ly de-sign . Thy dross to con-sume, and thy gold to re-

fled? Who un-to the Sav-iour for ref-uge have fled?
hand, Up-held by My right-eous, Om-ni-po-tent hand.
tress, And sanc-ti-fy to thee thy deep-est dis-tress.
fine, Thy dross to con-sume, and thy gold to re-fine.

St. Alban

J. S. B. Monsell

Arr. from Franz Josef Haydn

1. Earth be-low is teem-ing, Heav'n is bright a-bove; Ev-'ry brow is
2. For the sun and show-ers, For the rain and dew, For the nur-turing
3. Earth's broad har-vest whit-ens In a bright-er sun Than the orb that

beam-ing In the light of love; Ev-'ry eye re-joi-ces,
hours Spring and Sum-mer knew; For the gold-en Au-tumn,
light-ens All we tread up-on; Send out la-b'rers, Fa-ther!

Ev-'ry thought is praise; Hap-py hearts and voi-ces,
And its pre-cious stores, For the love that brought them
Where fields rip-'ning wave, All the na-tions gath-er,

REFRAIN

Glad-den nights and days. O Al-might-y Giv-er! Boun-ti-ful and
Teem-ing to our doors.
Gath-er in and save.

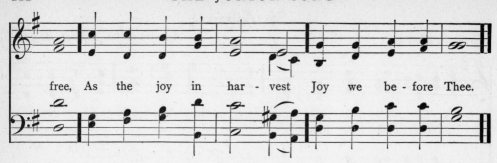

free, As the joy in har - vest Joy we be - fore Thee.

Truro

O. B. Frothingham

Charles Burney (?)

1. Thou Lord of hosts, whose guid - ing hand Has brought us
2. Those spir - its lay their no - blest pow'rs, As of - f'rings
3. Send down Thy con - stant aid, we pray; Be Thy pure

here, be - fore Thy face, Our spir - its wait for
on . Thy . ho - ly shrine; Thine was the strength that
an - gels . with us still; Thy truth,— be that our

Thy com - mand, Our si - lent hearts im - plore Thy peace.
nour - ished ours; The sol - diers of . the . cross are Thine.
firm - est . stay; Our on - ly rest, to . do Thy will.

Alford

Henry Alford

John B. Dykes

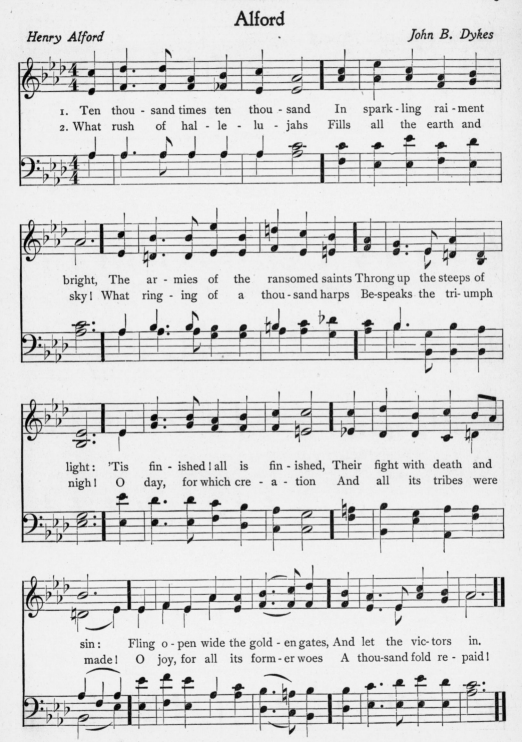

1. Ten thou - sand times ten thou - sand In spark - ling rai - ment
2. What rush of hal - le - lu - jahs Fills all the earth and

bright, The ar - mies of the ransomed saints Throng up the steeps of
sky! What ring - ing of a thou - sand harps Be-speaks the tri - umph

light: 'Tis fin - ished! all is fin - ished, Their fight with death and
nigh! O day, for which cre - a - tion And all its tribes were

sin: Fling o - pen wide the gold - en gates, And let the vic - tors in.
made!   O joy, for all its form - er woes A thou-sand fold re - paid!

St. Leonard

Adelaide A. Proctor   *Henry Hiles*

1. The shad-ows of the eve-ning hours Fall from the dark-'ning
2. Slow-ly the rays of day-light fade; So fade with-in our
3. Let peace, O Lord, Thy peace, O God, Up-on our souls de-

sky; Up-on the fra-grance of the flow'rs The dews of eve-ning
heart The hopes in earth-ly love and joy, That one by one de-
scend; From mid-night fears, and per-ils, Thou Our trem-bling hearts de-

lie. Be-fore Thy throne, O Lord of heav'n, We kneel at close of
part. Slow-ly the bright stars, one by one, With-in the heav-ens
fend. Give us a res-pite from our toil; Calm and sub-due our

day; Look on Thy chil-dren from on high, And hear us while we pray.
shine; Give us, O Lord, fresh hopes in heav n, And trust in things di-vine.
woes; Thro' the long day we la-bor, Lord, Oh, give us now re-pose.

Naomi

Anna Steele
Alt. by Rev. A. M. Toplady

Hans G. Nägeli
Arr. by Lowell Mason

1. Fa - ther, what-e'er of . earth - ly bliss Thy sov'reign will de - nies,
2. Give me a calm, a . thank - ful heart, From ev - 'ry mur-mur free;
3. Let the sweet hope that Thou art mine My path of life at - tend;

Ac - cept-ed at Thy throne of grace, Let this pe - ti - tion rise:
The bless-ings of Thy grace im - part, And let me live to Thee.
Thy pres-ence thro' my jour - ney shine, And bless its hap - py end.

Mornington

Henry F. Lyte

Earl of Mornington

1. Sing to the Lord, our might, With ho - ly fer - vor sing;
2. We still, like them of old, Are in the wil - der - ness;
3. Then let us o - pen wide Our hearts for Him to fill;

Let hearts and in - stru-ments u - nite To praise our heav'n-ly King.
And God is still as near His fold, To pit - y and to bless.
And He that Is - rael then sup - plied, Will help His Is - rael still.

The Star-Spangled Banner
(SERVICE VERSION)

Francis Scott Key   *John Stafford Smith*
Con spirito

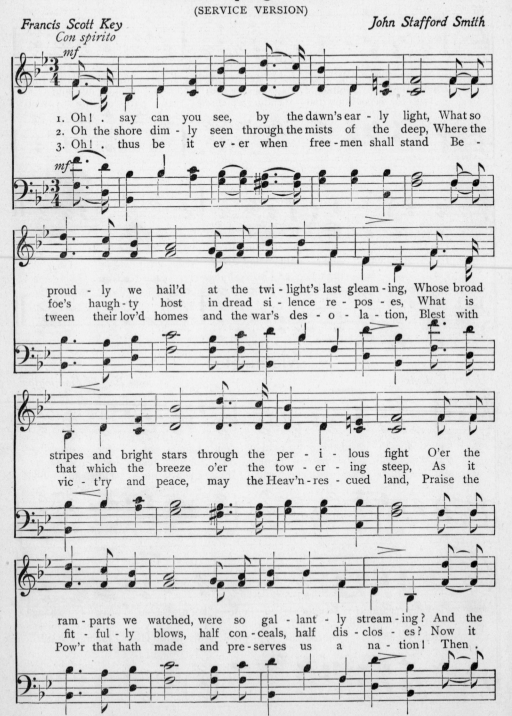

1. Oh! . say can you see, by the dawn's ear - ly light, What so
2. Oh the shore dim - ly seen through the mists of the deep, Where the
3. Oh! . thus be it ev - er when free - men shall stand Be -

proud - ly we hail'd at the twi - light's last gleam - ing, Whose broad
foe's haugh - ty host in dread si - lence re - pos - es, What is
tween their lov'd homes and the war's des - o - la - tion, Blest with

stripes and bright stars through the per - i - lous fight O'er the
that which the breeze o'er the tow - er - ing steep, As it
vic - t'ry and peace, may the Heav'n - res - cued land, Praise the

ram - parts we watched, were so gal - lant - ly stream - ing? And the
fit - ful - ly blows, half con - ceals, half dis - clos - es? Now it
Pow'r that hath made and pre - serves us a na - tion! Then .

rock - et's red glare, the bombs burst - ing in air, Gave
catch - es the gleam of the morn - ing's first beam, In full
con - quer we must, when our cause it is just, And

proof thro' the night that our flag was still there. Oh!
glo - ry re - flect - ed, now shines on the stream. 'Tis the
this be our mot - to, "In God is our trust!" And the

say does that star - span - gled ban - ner still wave
star - span - gled ban - ner, oh, long may it wave
star - span - gled ban - ner in tri - umph shall wave

O'er the land of the free and the home of the brave!

Columbia, the Gem of the Ocean

Timothy Dwight

David T. Shaw

Con spirito

1. O Co-lum - bia! the gem of the o - cean, The home of the brave and the free, . . The shrine of each pa - triot's de - vo - tion, A world of - fers hom - age to thee. . . Thy man - dates make he - roes as -

2. When war wing'd its wide des - o - la - tion, And threat-ened the land to de - form, . . The ark then of free-dom's foun-da - tion, Co - lum - bia, rode safe thro' the storm; . . With the gar - lands of vic - t'ry a -

3. The star - span-gled ban - ner bring hith - er, O'er Co - lum-bia's true sons let it wave; . . May the wreathes they have won nev-er with - er, Nor its stars cease to shine on the brave; . . May the ser - vice u - nit - ed ne'er

sem - ble, When Lib - er - ty's form stands in
round her, When so proud - ly she bore her brave
sev - er, But hold to their col - ors so

view; ... Thy ban-ners make tyr-an-ny tremble, When
crew; ... With her flag proud-ly float-ing be-fore her, The
true; ... The ar-my and na-vy for-ev-er, Three

borne by the red, white and blue. ... When borne by the red, white and
boast of the red, white and blue. ... The boast of the red, white and
cheers for the red, white and blue. ... Three cheers for the red, white and

blue, When borne by the red, white and
blue, The boast of the red, white and
blue, Three cheers for the red, white and

blue, white and blue,

blue, ... Thy . ban - ners make tyr - an - ny
blue, ... With her flag proud - ly float - ing be -
blue, ... The . ar - my and na - vy for -

blue, white and blue,

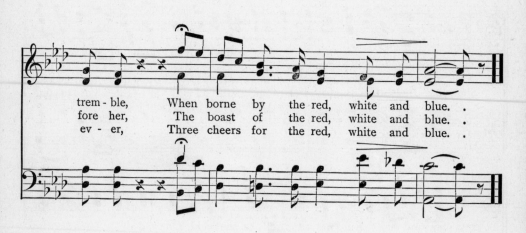

trem - ble,   When borne by   the red, white and blue. .
fore her,   The boast of   the red, white and blue. .
ev - er,   Three cheers for   the red, white and blue. .

The American Hymn

Mathias Keller   *Mathias Keller*
Maestoso

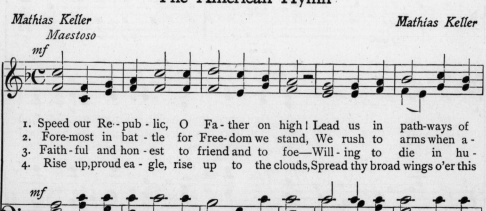

1. Speed our Re - pub - lic, O Fa - ther on high! Lead us in   path-ways of
2. Fore-most in bat - tle for Free-dom we stand, We rush to   arms when a -
3. Faith - ful and hon - est to friend and to foe—Will - ing to   die in hu -
4. Rise up, proud ea - gle, rise up to the clouds, Spread thy broad wings o'er this

jus - tice and right; Rul - ers as well as the ruled, "One and all,"
roused by its call; Still as of yore, when George Washing-ton led,
man - i - ty's cause— Thus we de - fy all ty - ran - ni - cal pow'r,
fair west - ern world; Fling from thy beak our dear ban - ner of old —

Gir - dle with vir - tue the ar - mor of might! Hail! three times hail to our
Thunders our war - cry: We con - quer or fall! Hail! three times hail to our
While we con - tend for our Un - ion and laws! Hail! three times hail to our
Show that it still is for free - dom un-furl'd! Hail! three times hail to our

coun - try and flag! Rul - ers as well as the ruled, "One and all," Gir - dle with
coun - try and flag! Still as of yore, when George Washington led, Thunders our
coun - try and flag! Thus we de - fy all ty - ran - ni - cal pow'r, While we con -
coun - try and flag! Fling from thy beak our dear ban - ner of old —Show that it

vir - tue the ar - mor of might! Hail! three times hail to our coun - try and flag!
war - cry: We con - quer or fall! Hail! three times hail to our coun - try and flag!
tend for our Un - ion and laws! Hail! three times hail to our coun - try and flag!
still is for Free - dom un-furl'd! Hail! three times hail to our coun - try and flag!

The Marseillaise

Rouget de Lisle

1. Ye sons of France, a-wake to glo - ry! O hark! what
2. O free - dom fair, we'll ne'er re - sign . thee, O sure de -

myr - iads bid you rise! Your chil - dren, wives, and grand - sires
liv - 'rer, glo - rious fame! Can dun - geon bolts and bars con -

hoar - y, Be - hold their tears, and hear their cries! Be - hold their
fine thee? Can aught thy no - ble spir - it . tame? Can aught thy

tears, and hear their cries! Shall cru - el ty - rants, mis - chief
no - ble spir - it . tame? Too long the world has wept, be -

breed - ing, With hire - ling hosts, a law - less band, Af -
wail - ing The ruth - less sword that ty - rants wield; But

fright and des - o - late the land, When peace and lib - er - ty lie
free - dom is our sword and shield, And all their arts are un - a -

bleed-ing? To arms, . to arms, ye brave! Th' a - veng - ing sword un -
vail - ing! To arms, . to arms, ye brave! Th' a - veng - ing sword un -

sheathe! March on, march on, all hearts resolved On vic - to-ry or death!

The Maple Leaf Forever

Alexander Muir   Alexander Muir

1. In days of yore from Bri - tain's shore, Wolfe, the daunt - less
2. At Queen - ston Heights and Lun - dy's Lane Our brave fa - thers,
3. On mer - ry Eng - land's far - famed land May kind Heav - en

he - ro came, And plant - ed firm Bri - tan - nia's flag On
side by side, For free - dom, homes, and loved ones dear, Firm - ly
sweet - ly smile; God bless old Scot - land ev - er - more, And

Can - a - da's fair do - main. Here may it wave, our boast and pride, And
stood and no - bly died; And those dear rights which they maintained, We
Ire - land's Em - er - ald Isle! Then swell the song, both loud and long, Till

joined in love to - geth - er, The Lil - y, This - tle, Sham-rock, Rose, And
swear to yield them nev-er! Our watchword ev - er - more shall be, The
rocks and for - ests quiv-er, God save our King and Heav - en bless The

Ma-ple Leaf for - ev -er! The Ma-ple Leaf, our emblem dear, The Ma-ple Leaf for -

ev - er! God save our King, and Heav - en bless The Ma - ple Leaf for - ev -er!

Italian National Hymn

1. All for - ward! All for - ward! All for - ward to bat - tle! The
2. All for - ward! All for - ward! All for - ward for Free - dom! In

trum - pets are cry - ing, All for - ward! All for - ward! Our
ter - ri - ble splen - dor She comes to the loy - al who

old   flag   is   fly - ing, When lib - er - ty   calls   us   we
die   to   de - fend   her; Her   stars   and   her   stripes   o'er   the

cres.

lin - ger   no   lon - ger,   Ye   reb - els,   come on!   tho'   a
wild   wave   of   bat - tle,   Shall float   in   the   heav - ens   to

cres.

_mp_

thou - sand   to   one!   Lib - er - ty!   Lib - er - ty!   death-less   and
wel - come us   on.   All   for - ward!   to   glo - ry   tho'   life - blood   is

glo - rious,   Un - der   the   ban - ner   thy   sons   are   vic -
pour - ing, Where bright swords   are   flash - ing,   and   can - nons   are

to - rious,   Free souls are   val - iant and   strong arms are
roar - ing.   Wel - come to   death in   the   bul - let's quick

stron - ger,   God   shall   go   with   us,   till   vic - t'ry be
rat - tle,   Fight - ing or   fall - ing shall free - dom be

won.   Hur - rah   for   the   ban - ner!   Hur - rah   for   the
won.   Hur - rah   for   the   ban - ner!   Hur - rah   for   the

ban - ner!   Hur - rah   for   the   ban - ner, the flag   of   the free!
ban - ner!   Hur - rah   for   the   ban - ner, the flag   of   the free!

God Ever Glorious

Joukowsky   *Alexis F. Lwoff*

1. God ev - er glo - ri - ous, Sov' - reign of
2. Still may Thy bless - ings rest, Fa - ther most

na - tions, Wav - ing the ban - ner of peace o'er the
ho - ly, O - ver each moun - tain, rock, riv - er and

land. Thine is the vic - to - ry, Thine is the sal -
shore. Sing hal - le - lu - jah, Shout in loud ho -

va - tion, Strong to de - liv - er, Own we Thine hand.
san - nas, God keep our coun - try Free ev - er - more.

America

Rev. Samuel F. Smith

Henry Carey (?)

Maestoso

1. My coun-try! 'tis of thee, Sweet land of lib-er-ty,
2. My na-tive coun-try, thee—Land of the no-ble free,
3. Let mu-sic swell the breeze, And ring from all the trees
4. Our fa-thers' God! to Thee, Au-thor of lib-er-ty,

Of thee I sing; Land where my fa-thers died! Land of the
Thy name I love; I love thy rocks and rills, Thy woods and
Sweet free-dom's song; Let mor-tal tongues a-wake, Let all that
To Thee we sing! Long may our land be bright With free-dom's

Pil-grim's pride! From ev-'ry moun-tain side Let free-dom ring.
tem-pled hills; My heart with rap-ture thrills Like that a-bove.
breathe par-take, Let rocks their si-lence break, The sound pro-long.
ho-ly light! Pro-tect us by Thy might, Great God, our King!

God Save the King

1 God save our gracious King,
Long live our noble King,
  God save the King!
Send him victorious,
Happy and glorious,
Long to reign over us;
  God save the King!

2 Thy choicest gifts in store
On him be pleas'd to pour,
  Long may he reign!
May he defend our laws,
And ever give us cause
To sing with heart and voice
  God save the King!

3 To ev'ry future age
Shall story's brightest page
  His fame declare:
How he bade discord cease,
Knowledge and Wealth increase,
And made the arts of Peace
  His constant care.

4 See all his people throng
To form a rampart strong
  Round our lov'd King;
And should a foe draw near,
Then all the world shall hear
Rise from our land the cheer,
  God save the King!

TERMS AND SIGNS OF EXPRESSION[1]

Accelerando (ăt-chä-lä-rän′dŏ), accelerating.

Adagio (ȧ-dä′jŏ), slow ; literally, at leisure.

Ad libitum (ăd lĭb′ĭ-tŭm), at the pleasure of the performer.

Agitato (ä-jĭ-tä′tō), agitated, perturbed ; indicates a hurried and broken style of performance.

Al (äl), to the ; at the; up to.

Al fine (fē′nĕ), to the end.

Alla marcia (äl′lä mär′chiȧ), in the manner of a march.

Allegretto (äl-lä-grăt′tŏ), less quick than *allegro ;* diminutive of *allegro.*

Allegro (äl-lä′grŏ), quick, lively ; literally, cheerful.

Andante (än-dän′tä), slow, graceful ; moving at a moderate pace ; literally, walking.

Andantino (än-dän-tē′nŏ), the diminutive of *andante*, and indicating here quicker *tempo.*

Animato (ȧ-nĕ-mä′tŏ), animated.

Assai (äs-sä′ĕ), very.

A tempo (ä tĕm′pŏ), return to first rate of speed.

Ben marcato (bĕn mär-kä′tŏ), well marked.

Brillante (brĕl-län′tä), brilliant, sparkling.

Cantabile (kȧn-tä′bĕ-lä), in a singing style, or very *legato.*

Colla voce (kŏl′lä vō′chä), with the voice ; *i.e.* taking the time from the singer.

Con anima (kōn ä′nĕ-mä), with animation.

Con brio (kōn brē′ŏ), with vigor, spirit, force.

Con espressione (kōn ăs-präs-sĕ-ō′nä), with expression.

Con grazia (kōn grä′tsĕ-ȧ), with grace.

Con moto (kōn mō′tŏ), with spirited movement.

Con moto di barcarolla (kōn mō′tŏ dē bär-kȧ-rō′lȧ), with the movement of a boating song.

Con moto di schottische (kōn mō′tŏ dē shŏt′tĭsh), with the movement of a schottische.

Con spirito (kōn spē′rĕ-tŏ), with spirit, energy.

Con tenerezza (kōn tĕn-ȧ-rĕt′sȧ), with tenderness.

————— **Crescendo** (krä-shăn′dŏ), gradually increasing the tone.

————— **Decrescendo** (dä-krä-shăn′dŏ) ; **diminuendo** (dĕ-mĕ-nōō-än′dŏ), gradually lessening the tone.

Dolce (dŏl′chä), sweet, soft.

E (ä), and.

Energico (ȧ-när′jĕ-kŏ), energetic, forcible.

Espressivo (ăs-präs-sĕ′vŏ), with expression.

f, forte (fôr′tä), loud.

ff, fortissimo (fôr-tĕs′sĕ-mŏ), very loud.

fz, forzando (fôr-tsän′dŏ), sharply emphasized.

Giocoso (jŏ-kŏ′sŏ), humorous, playful.

Giojoso (jŏ-yŏ′sŏ), joyous.

Giusto (jōōs′tŏ), in just, exact time.

Grandioso (grȧn-dĕ-ō′sŏ), grand, sonorous.

Grazioso (grä-tsĕ-ō′sŏ), graceful, elegant.

Larghetto (lär-găt′tŏ), rather slow ; the diminutive of *largo*, slow, or, literally, large.

Largo (lär′gŏ), slow, broad.

Legato (lä-gä′tŏ), even, continuous, flowing ; literally, tied.

Leggiero (läd-jĕ-ȧ′rŏ), light.

Lento (lăn′tŏ), literally, slow.

Lusingando (lōō′zĕn-gän′dŏ), coaxingly, persuasively.

Maestoso (mä-ĕs-tō′zŏ), with dignity, majesty.

Marcato (mär-kä′tŏ), distinct, emphasized ; literally, marked.

Marziale (mär-tsĕ-ä′lä), martial, in the style of a march.

Meno (mä′nŏ), less.

Meno mosso (mä′nŏ mŏs′sŏ), less speed, less fast.

mf, mezzo forte (mĕd′zŏ fôr′tä), half loud.

Minuetto (mē-nōō-ăt′tŏ), a minuet.

Misterioso (mĕs-tä-rĕ-ō′sŏ), mysterious.

Moderato (mŏd-ĕ-rä′tŏ), moderate.

Molto (mŏl′tŏ), much, very.

Morendo (mō-rĕn′dŏ), dying away, growing fainter and fainter.

mp, mezzo piano (mĕd′zŏ pĕ-ä′nŏ), half soft.

Non troppo (nōn trŏp′pŏ), not too much.

Pensieroso (pĕn-sĕ-ĕ-rō′sŏ), thoughtful, pensive.

Più (pĕ-ṳ′), a little more.

Poco (pō′kŏ), little ; **poco a poco**, gradually.

Poco più moto (pō′kŏ pĕ-ṳ′ mō′tŏ), somewhat faster.

pp, pianissimo (pē′ȧ-nĭs′sĭ-mŏ), very soft.

p, piano (pĕ-ä′nŏ), soft.

Presto (prĕs′tŏ), fast, in rapid *tempo ;* usually one beat to the measure ; literally, quick.

Rallentando (räl-lĕn-tän′dŏ), becoming slower; literally, abating. Abb. *rall.*

Religioso (rä′lĕ-jō′sŏ), solemn, devout.

Rinf., rinforzando (rĭn-fôr-tsän′dŏ), suddenly emphasized and accented.

Risoluto (rē-zŏ-lōō′tŏ), energetic, decided.

Ritardando (rē′tär-dän′dŏ), slower ; literally, retarding. Abb. *rit.*

Riten., ritenuto (rē′tȧ-nōō′tŏ), immediately slower.

Scherzando (skĕr-tsän′dŏ), sportive, playful.

Semplice (sĕm′plĕ-chä), simple.

Sempre (sĕm′prä), always, continually.

Sforzando (sfôr-tsän′dŏ) (>), with special emphasis.

Sostenuto (sŏs-tä-nōō′tŏ), sustained.

Spiritoso (spē-rĕ-tō′sŏ), spirited.

Stringendo (strĭn-jĕn′dŏ), hastening, accelerating the movement, usually suddenly with an accompanying increase in power of tone.

Tempo di valse (tĕm′pŏ dē väl′sȧ), in the time of a waltz.

Tenuto (tä-noo′tō), held, sustained. Abbr. *ten.*

Tranquillamente (trän-kwĕl-lä-măn′tä), calmly, quietly.

Tranquillo (trän-kwĕl′lŏ), tranquil, quiet.

Veloce (vȧ-lō′chä), swiftly.

Vivace (vĕ-vä′chä), gay ; literally, lively.

Vivo (vē′vŏ), animated.

COMPOSERS REPRESENTED IN THIS VOLUME

Abt, Franz, *eminent composer,* celebrated for a remarkable melodic facility; born, 1819; died, 1885.

Adams, Eugene, American musician.

Allan, Robert, American musician; born, 1877, in Maine.

Arnold, Samuel, English, *noted composer*; born, 1740, at London; died at London, 1802.

Avery, Stanley R., American musician; born, 1879, at Yonkers, New York.

Barnby, Sir Joseph, English, *eminent composer*; born, 1838, at York; died, 1896, at London.

Batiste, Edouard, French, *noted composer*; born, 1820, at Paris; died, 1876, at Paris.

Beethoven, Ludwig van, *great composer,* "The Father of Modern Instrumental Music"; born, 1770; died, 1827.

Bellingham, M., American musician.

Boyd, C. E., American musician; born, 1856, at Cambridge, Massachusetts.

Brunt, Phyllis, American musician.

Burney, Charles, English, *noted composer*; born, 1726, at Shrewsbury; died at Chelsea, England, 1814.

Carey, Henry, English; born, 1690; died, 1743, at London.

Coenen, Willem, Dutch, *noted composer*; born, 1837, at Rotterdam.

Crane, Mary Eloise, American musician.

Cushman, Estelle, American musician; born, 1891, in Massachusetts.

Dalcroze, Émile Jaques, Swiss, *eminent composer*; born, 1865, at Vienna.

Dibdin, Charles, English, *eminent composer*; born, 1745, at Southampton, England; died, 1814, at London.

Donizetti, Gaetano, Italian, *eminent composer*; a brilliant operatic composer; born, 1797, at Bergamo, Italy; died at Bergamo, 1848.

Dykes, John B., English, *noted composer*; born, 1823, at Kingston-upon-Hull, England; died at St. Leonards, 1876.

Faye, Elizabeth, American musician.

Foster, Stephen Collins, American, *noted composer*; born, 1826, near Pittsburgh, Pennsylvania; died at New York, 1864.

Gartlan, George H., American musician; born, 1882, at New York.

Gould, John E., American, *noted composer*; born, 1812, in Maine; died, 1875, in Africa.

Gounod, Charles François, French, *great composer*; composer of "Faust"; born, 1818, at Paris; died at Paris, 1893.

Gow, George Colman, American musician; born, 1860, at Ayer Junction, Massachusetts.

Grieg, Edvard, Norwegian, *great composer,* "The Greatest Norwegian Composer"; born, 1843, at Bergen, Norway; died at Bergen, 1907.

Hadley, Henry Kimball, American, *noted composer*; born, 1871, at Somerville, Massachusetts.

Handel, George Frederick, *great composer,* "The Greatest Choral Composer"; born, 1685; died, 1759, at London.

Haydn, Franz Josef, *great composer,* "The Father of the Symphony"; born, 1732; died 1809.

Hiles, Henry, English, *noted composer*; born, 1826, at Shrewsbury; died at Worthing, 1904.

Hoffer, S., American musician; born, 1864, in Vermont.

Hölzel, Gustav, musician.

Hopkins, Edward J., English, *noted composer*; born, 1818, at Westminster; died at London, 1901.

Johnstone, Arthur Edward, American musician; born, 1860, at London, England.

Kaillmark, E., American musician.

Kendall, Arthur Sherwood, American musician; born, 1853, at Boston, Massachusetts.

Kittredge, Walter, American musician.

Krüger, Rudolph, American musician.

Kücken, Friedrich Wilhelm, *noted composer*; born, 1810; died, 1882.

Lansen, M., American musician.

Lwoff, Alexis Feodorovitch, Russian, *noted composer*; born, 1799, at Reval; died on estate in Kovno, 1870.

Maker, Frederick C., English musician; born, 1844.

Marie, Gabriel, French, *noted composer*; born, 1852, at Paris.

Mendelssohn, Felix, *great composer*; celebrated for popularizing the best in music; born, 1809; died, 1847.

Meyer, Pauline A., American musician; born, 1890, at Providence, R.I.

Meyer-Helmund, Erik, Russian, *noted composer*; born, 1861, at Petrograd.

Mornington, Garret Colley Wellesley, Earl of, Irish, *noted composer*; born, 1735, at Dangan, Ireland; died at Kensington, London, 1781.

Moszkowski, Moritz, Polish, *eminent composer*; born, 1854, at Breslau, Silesia.

Mozart, Wolfgang Amadeus, *great composer*, unexcelled in the purity, grace, and spontaneity of his music; born, 1756; died, 1791.

Nägeli, Hans Georg, Swiss, *noted composer*; born, 1773, at Wetzikon, near Zurich; died at Wetzikon, 1836.

Nevin, Arthur, American, *noted composer*; born, 1871, at Edgeworth, Pennsylvania.

Osborne, Mabel C., American musician; born, 1885, at Fayetteville, New York.

Pinsuti, Ciro, Italian, *eminent composer*; born, 1829, at Florence; died at Florence, 1888.

Remsen, F., American musician.

Roeder, Otto, musician.

Rouget de Lisle, Claude Joseph, French, *noted composer*; born, 1760, at Lons-le-Saunier, Jura; died at Choisy-le-Roi, 1836.

Schubert, Franz Peter, *great composer*; "The Famous Lyric Composer"; born, 1797; died 1828.

Schumann, Robert, *great composer*; a genius in the creation of melody and new ideals for the pianoforte and voice; born, 1810; died, 1856.

Shaw, David T., American musician.

Shaw, Frederick, American musician.

Silcher, Friedrich, *noted composer*; born, 1789; died, 1860.

Smart, Henry, English, *eminent composer*; born, 1813, at London; died at London, 1879.

Smith, Isaac, English, *noted composer*; born, 1735, at London; died there, 1800.

Targett, Arthur B., American musician; born, 1876, at Cohoes, New York.

Tosti, Francesco Paolo, Italian, *eminent composer*; born, 1846, at Ortona, Abruzzi.

Towner, Earl, American musician; born, 1890, at Latah, Washington.

Tschaikowsky, Peter Ilyitch, Russian, *great composer*; "The Greatest Russian Composer"; born, 1840, at Wotkinsk, province of Wjätka; died at Petrograd, 1893.

Verdi, Giuseppi, Italian, *great composer*; "The Greatest Composer of Italian Opera"; born, 1813, at Le Roncole in the Duchy of Parma, Italy; died at Milan, 1901.

Weidt, K., Swiss musician; born, 1857, at Bern.

Wesley, Samuel S., English, *noted composer*; born, 1810, at London; died at Gloucester, 1876.

White, Wilson, American musician; born, 1872, at Buffalo, New York.

Wilhelm, Carl, *noted composer*; born, 1815; died, 1873.

Williams, Aaron, Welsh, *noted composer*; born, 1734; died, 1776.

Wilson, L. S., American musician; born, 1880, in Illinois.

MUSICAL FORMS REPRESENTED IN THIS VOLUME

VOCAL

SONG: a melody or tune united with lyric or narrative verse is a Song. For example, see page 5, " Love Your Neighbor."

Folk Song: a song that has originated among the people and has been extensively used by them is called a Folk Song. It is often based on a legendary or historical event or on some incident of common life. A song written in imitation of these simple and artless songs is also called a Folk Song. For example of a Folk Song, see page 79, " All Through the Night."

Folk Songs are of many nationalities and show strong racial characteristics. The following are typical representations of these nationalities:

English, page 103, "The Spring is Coming."
Italian, page 16, "The Music of the Brook."
Russian, page 26, "The Cossack's Lullaby."
Irish, page 77, "The Harp That Once Through Tara's Halls."
Welsh, page 105, "Cavalier Song."
Norwegian, page 73, "The Willow and the Oak."
Finnish, page 140, "Whisper, Whisper."
Scotch, page 152, "Loch Lomond."
French, page 7, "The Noël Star."
American, page 170, "Old Folks at Home."

Popular Song: a song which is in vogue among all classes and yet compared with a Folk Song is of more recent origin may be called a Popular Song. While in many instances the distinction between a Folk Song and a Popular Song may be slight, yet as a general thing the Popular Song is a little more elaborate than the Folk Song. For example, see page 206, " Sweet and Low," by Barnby.

Strophe Song: a song in which all stanzas are sung to the same music is a Strophe Song. For example, see page 175, "O Sea, How Fair Art Thou."

Ballad: a simple song in strophe form which is descriptive or tells a story is a Ballad. For example, see page 156, " On Venice Waters."

National or Patriotic Song: a song identified with the history of a nation either by sentiment or by long use is a National Song. For example, see page 239, " America."

College Song: a song which for a long time has been in general use by college students is a College Song. For example, see page 208, " There's Music in the Air."

Song for Unison Chorus: any song in which all voices sing the melody, either in unison or an octave apart, may be called a Song for Unison Chorus. For example, see page 1, " March of Triumph."

Art Song: a song in which each verse of the poem has an appropriate musical setting, or, in other words, a song in which the music reflects and interprets the meaning of the poem throughout and does not repeat with each stanza is an Art Song. Furthermore, it is a song which is the product of cultivated musical taste and inspiration. For example, see page 162, "To the Hermit Thrush," by Tosti.

CONCERTED MUSIC: music in which several parts are sung (or played) harmoniously at the same time is called Concerted Music. For example, see page 154, " Hymn of Freedom," by Donizetti.

Two-part Song: a two-part musical composition in which the second part is merely a supporting accompaniment is a Two-part Song. For example, see page 20, " Long Live Valor," by Donizetti.

Trio: a three-part composition is a trio. For example, see page 34, " Rest," by Abt.

Quartet: a four-part composition is a quartet. For example, see page 198, " The Bugle Song," by Henry Hadley.

Part Song: a composition of three or more parts in which the lower parts serve merely as an accompaniment is a Part Song. For example, see page 172, " What Have We Done To-Day," by Arthur Targett.

Hymn: a short part song expressing devotion or praise is a Hymn. For example, see page 223, " Alford."

Part Song Chorus: a part song with more than one voice on each part may be called a Part Song Chorus.

OPERA: a versified drama, or play, set to music for voices and instruments is an Opera. Any part of the music of an Opera may be called operatic music. For example, see page 127, "Chorus of Pilgrims," from the opera "I Lombardi," by Verdi.

Grand Opera: a serious opera in which there is no spoken dialogue is a Grand Opera. For an example of an excerpt from Grand Opera see page 100, "O What Joy," from the Grand Opera "Faust," by Gounod.

INSTRUMENTAL

Song Form: an instrumental melody in slow tempo or a short cycle of such melodies may be called Song Form. For example, see page 56, "Watchman's Song," by Grieg.

Theme: a musical period or a melody used as a subject, like the text of a discourse, is a Theme. For example, see page 3, "Slumber Song," by Schumann.

Minuet or Dance Form: a stately and graceful form in three-quarter measure, consisting of a first theme, a second theme, and the first theme restated, is a Minuet. For example, see page 145, "The Garden by the Sea," a minuet by Beethoven.

Sonata: the most important instrumental form is the Sonata. It is distinguished by being a com-plete musical whole in several separate parts or "movements," which are in various related keys. The Sonata is thus like a story with various chapters. The close thread of connection is often shown most strikingly by the very contrast of these movements.

The Sonata has usually four movements which really express four moods. These moods may be typified roughly thus: Aspiration, Meditation, Humor, Triumph.

Music for two or more solo instruments, usu-ally written in the form of a Sonata, is called Chamber Music. For example of an excerpt from Chamber Music, see page 184, "Spirit of Peace," by Beethoven.

Concerto: a composition for a solo instrument with full orchestra, based in form upon the sonata, is called a Concerto. For example of an excerpt from Concerto music, see page 120, "On the Mountain," by Mendelssohn.

Waltz: a moderately slow dance form in three-quarter measure is a Waltz. For example, see page 10, "Fairy Revels," by Johnstone.

Schottische: a moderately slow dance form in four-quarter measure is a Schottische. For example, see page 41, "A Folk Dance," by Gabriel Marie.

March: a composition of strongly marked rhythm, designed for timing the steps of a body of persons in marching, is a March. For example, see page 54, "A Match Game," by S. Hoffer.

INDEX OF MUSICAL FORMS AND COMPOSERS

SUGGESTED MUSICAL PROGRAMS

Those teachers who use the Junior Song and Chorus Book will have no occasion to look elsewhere for music for exhibition purposes, for in all music they will be able to find nothing more attractive than the selections in this book. In making the choice of this material the guiding principle of the editors was " What is not good enough for a concert program is not good enough for everyday class work."

We suggest below a few musical programs. The choice of selections has been governed by the desire to present the greatest variety in musical form and mood. These programs are designed to serve as a guide to the teacher in making up similar programs from the remainder of the selections in the book, which are equally meritorious for such a purpose.

PROGRAM NO. 1

1. Operatic Selection: " Chorus of Pilgrims " (p. 127) . . . . Giuseppe Verdi
Four parts, mixed voices

2. Boating Song: " Fair Napoli " (p. 95) . . . . Italian Folk Tune
Three parts, with bass ad lib.

3. (a) " Sunrise " (p. 4) . . . . M. Lansen
(b) " Love your Neighbor " (p. 5) . . . . Émile Jaques Dalcroze
Three parts, unchanged voices

4. " Spirit of Peace," from Opus 97 (p. 184) . . . . Ludwig van Beethoven
Four parts, mixed voices

5. Vocal Waltz: " Fairy Revels " (p. 10) . . . . Arthur Edward Johnstone
Three parts, girls' voices

6. Field Song: " The Match Game " (p. 54) . . . . S. Hoffer
Unison chorus, boys' voices

7. Popular Song: " The Old Oaken Bucket " (p. 178) . . . . E. Kaillmark
Melody by boys, vocal accompaniment by girls

8. Patriotic Song: " America the Beautiful " (p. 97) . . . . Arthur S. Kendall
Four parts, mixed chorus

PROGRAM NO. 2

1. Quartet: " Eldorado " (p. 135) . . . . Ciro Pinsuti
Four parts, mixed voices

2. (a) " The Music of the Brook " (p. 16) . . . . Italian Folk Tune
(b) " Slumber Song " (p. 3) . . . . Robert Schumann
Three parts, unchanged voices

3. Old English Popular Song: "Tinker's Song" (p. 74) . . . . Charles Dibdin

Unison chorus, boys' voices

4. Part Song: "What Have We Done To-Day" (p. 172) . . . . Arthur B. Targett

Four parts, mixed voices

5. Art Song: "Lovely Spring" (p. 190) . . . . Willem Coenen

Three parts, with bass ad lib.

6. Operatic Duet: "Long Live Valor" (p. 20) . . . . Gaetano Donizetti

Girls' voices

7. (a) "Watchman's Song" (p. 56) . . . . Edvard Grieg
   (b) "Autumn Winds" (p. 80) . . . . Mary Eloise Crane

Soprano, alto, and bass

8. "Consolation," from Opus 15 (p. 147) . . . . Franz Schubert

Four parts, mixed chorus

PROGRAM NO. 3

1. Art Song: "Sing" (p. 82) . . . . Gustav Hölzel

Arranged for soprano, alto, and baritone

2. Strophe Song: "Thou Art Near Me, Margarita" (p. 188) . . . . . . Erik Meyer-Helmund

Three parts, with bass ad lib.

3. (a) "By the Fireside" (p. 23) . . . . Robert Allan
   (b) "Woodland Pictures" (p. 18) . . . . Wolfgang Amadeus Mozart

Three unchanged voices

4. "Morning Prayer," from Opus 39 (p. 116) . . . . Peter Tschaikowsky

Arranged for three parts, with bass ad lib.

5. Quartet: "The Bugle Song" (p. 198) . . . . Henry Hadley

Four parts, mixed voices

6. (a) "Cavalier Song" (p. 105) . . . . Welsh Folk Tune
   (b) "The Stormy Petrel" (p. 176) . . . . Wilson White

Four parts, mixed voices

7. Four-part Song: "Fair October" (p. 181) . . . . L. S. Wilson

Four parts, mixed voices

8. Male Chorus: "We Meet Again To-Night (p. 210) . . . . College Song

Four parts

9. Folk Song: "Old Folks at Home" (p. 170) . . . . Stephen C. Foster

Four parts, mixed voices

PROGRAM NO. 4

1. **Popular Song:** " Fair Cuba " (p. 109) . . . . Eduardo Sanchez des Fuentes
Three parts, with bass ad lib.

2. (*a*) " The Flowers' Lament " (p. 112) . . . . French Folk Tune
(*b*) " The Spring is Coming " (p. 103). . . . . English Folk Tune
Three parts, with bass ad lib.

3. **Vocal Schottische:** " Folk Dance " (p. 41) . . . . Gabriel Marie
Three unchanged voices

4. **Operatic Selection from " Faust ":** " O What Joy " (p. 100) . . . . Charles Gounod
Three parts, with bass ad lib.

5. **Vocal Minuet:** " The Garden by the Sea " (p. 145) . . . . Ludwig van Beethoven
Duet and four-part chorus

6. (*a*) " The Harp that Once Through Tara's Hall " (p. 77) . . . . . . Irish Folk Tune
(*b*) " On the Chapel Steps " (p. 89) . . . . George Colman Gow
Soprano, alto, and bass

7. **Berceuse:** " A Lullaby " (p. 93) . . . . Moritz Moszkowski
Three parts, with bass ad lib.

8. **Patriotic Song:** " The Star-Spangled Banner " (p. 226) . . . . Samuel Arnold
Four parts, mixed chorus

PROGRAM NO. 5

1. **Vocal March:** " March of Triumph " (p. 1) . . . . Arthur Nevin
Unison chorus

2. **Trio:** " Rest " (p. 34) . . . . Franz Abt
Unchanged voices

3. **Ballad:** " On Venice Waters " (p. 156) . . . . Otto Roeder
A bass and four-part chorus

4. **Art Song:** " To the Hermit Thrush " (p. 162) . . . . Francesco Paolo Tosti
Four parts, mixed voices

5. " On the Mountain," from Opus 64 (p. 120) . . . . Felix Mendelssohn
Three parts, with bass ad lib.

6. (*a*) " The Willow and the Oak " (p. 73) . . . . Norwegian Folk Tune
(*b*) " The Loreley " (p. 91) . . . . Folk Tune
Soprano, alto, and baritone

7. **Vocal Waltz:** " Vacation " (p. 28) . . . . L. S. Wilson
Girls' voices

8. **Operatic Selection:** " Hymn of Freedom " (p. 154) . . . . Gaetano Donizetti
Arranged for four parts, mixed chorus

ALPHABETICAL INDEX OF SONGS